Table of Contents

Unit III • MECHANICS

Unit IV • ELECTRICITY AND ATOMIC STRUCTURE

WAVE – PARTICLE

DUALITY

IN THE

LABORATORY

T.J.E. WOLFE

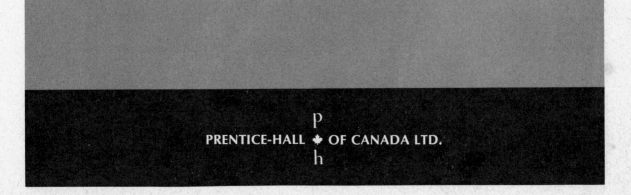

PRENTICE-HALL OF CANADA LTD.

Library of Congress Catalog Card No. 68-24133
94604

3 4 5 72
Printed and bound in Canada

Preface

Physics is the fundamental science whereby man studies the interactions of matter and energy in an attempt to explain the world around him. In the beginning man was mainly concerned with the visible world. With the birth of the nuclear age, however, man has become more concerned with the microscopic and submicroscopic nature of matter.

The main theme of this physics course is the wave-particle duality of radiation and matter. At the conclusion of the course, the wave and particle models of matter are applied to a description of the hydrogen atom, the simplest of all atoms.

Studies have shown that individuals learn best from firsthand experiences. An essential part of the understanding of physics thus occurs during experiments which are performed by the student. (The apparatus required per student group is indicated at the beginning of each experiment.)

The experiments in this manual have been written with this in mind. The student, however, is faced with a time problem. Because of this, sufficient guidance in the form of leading questions has been provided to enable the student to complete the experimental observations in the time available, with little guidance from the instructor. These questions will also permit the student to complete an experiment individually, at his own pace, and on his own time if necessary. It is hoped that enough original thought has been included to provide the student with problems and experiences similar to those faced by scientists. The Millikan Experiment has been included to challenge the top physics student and to present him with some of the difficulties experienced by any true scientist in taking accurate readings under difficult situations.

The author feels that an understanding of graphs, variables and functions is essential to the understanding of physics and that the data for graphical analysis should be obtained, where possible, from student experiments. A number of experiments have been included in Unit I to accomplish this. The student should be able to analyze the data obtained by plotting a graph, to replot the data if necessary in the form to produce a straight-line graph, and from this to write an equation describing the relationship between the variables under study.

Where suitable equipment is not available to perform classroom experiments, experimental data has been provided which will enable the student to reach valid conclusions.

Tables and spaces for sentence answers have been provided in the manual to enable the student to record the results of an experiment as they are taken without sacrificing time or technique. The three-hole punched format will enable the student to transfer these lab reports, including the associated graphs and sketches, directly into his classroom notes in the proper sequence, or the student may wish to place the lab reports in chronological order in a separate three-ring binder. The author feels, however, that the student should complete a formal report on at least one experiment performed during the year.

It is the author's hope that, in the majority of cases, the experiments will be performed preceding classroom discussion of the topic and will give the student a feeling of participating in the discoveries of science rather than verifying conclusions which are already known. This does not mean, however, that each student must perform all the experiments. The experiments completed should provide all students, including those who may never be exposed to a formal science course again, with a better understanding of the work and functions of the scientist. Perhaps this will contribute to some extent to the breakdown of the fears that the layman has of the scientist at the present time.

The author wishes to express his appreciation to J.C. Fraser and to his associates at Downsview Secondary School for their helpful criticisms, to R. Decent, G.B. Halpin, and P.B. Hunt of Prentice-Hall of Canada Ltd. for their assistance in editing and arranging the manuscript and diagrams, and to his wife, Barbara, for typing and preparing the manuscript and for aid in reading and checking.

T.J.E.W.

Unit I

TIME, SPACE AND MOTION

Fundamentals of Measurement

Variables, Functions and Graphs

Motion Along a Straight Line

Motion in Space

Fundamentals of Measurement

Expt. #1   SHORT TIME INTERVALS

Introduction   A stop watch will not adequately measure very small time intervals, such as the length of time required for one to-and-fro motion of the tong of a vibrating tuning fork. The error caused by the reaction time of the person operating the stop watch will be large compared to the time being measured. It is necessary to use an instrument such as a stroboscope to accurately measure smaller time intervals.

Purpose   To study the use of the stroboscope.

Part I   Demonstration

Apparatus

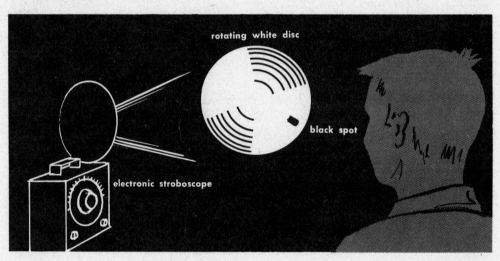

Method   1. Adjust the speed of the rotating disc until, with the stroboscope at a slow frequency, the black spot is "stopped" in one position. How many times do you see the black spot in one revolution?

Is the black spot going around only once in one look (flash) or more than once? Suggest a way of checking this.

2. Change the flash frequency of the stroboscope until the black spot is "stopped" in two positions. How many times is the black spot now visible in one revolution of the disc?

3. Decrease the frequency of the stroboscope until only one spot is seen in the "stopped" position. The flash frequency of the stroboscope is then equal to the frequency of the spot's rotation. To make sure that you have measured the frequency correctly after finding the rate that "stops" the motion, increase the flash frequency (look frequency) smoothly until the object is "stopped" in two positions. Then decrease the flash frequency to the first frequency below this that results in one "stopped" image. The frequency is correctly determined by the highest rotation rate that "stops" the motion in one position.

Class Experiment using Hand Stroboscope **Part II**

Apparatus

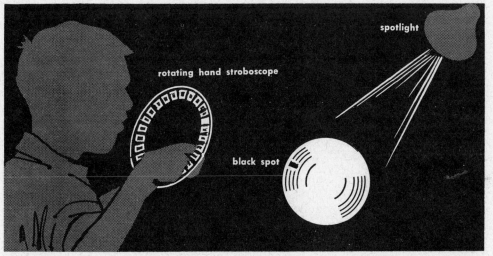

1. Seal with black tape all but one of the slits in the stroboscope. Hold the stroboscope in front of your eye and rotate it slowly while looking at the rotating white disc. The rotation of the black spot can be "stopped" at one point by varying the frequency of the hand stroboscope. Compare the time required for one rotation of the hand stroboscope with that for one rotation of the black spot when you have the motion "stopped."   **Method**

Is there any other frequency relationship for which the spot appears "stopped"? Explain.

2. With a stop watch, have your partner measure how long it takes you to complete 10 revolutions of the stroboscope when viewing one image of the black spot correctly "stopped." From this, determine the time in seconds for one rotation of the hand stroboscope.

3. After the instructor has increased the rate of rotation of the spot, again view it through the hand stroboscope and "stop" it as before. Measure the time for 10 revolutions of the stroboscope and calculate how long, in seconds, it takes the black spot to make one revolution.

4. Remove the tape from the slit of the stroboscope opposite the open one, and rotate it at the same frequency as above. How many images of the "stopped" black spot are now visible?

What would you have to do to get one image of the "stopped" spot?

Compare the time required to complete one revolution of the 2-slit stroboscope with the time required to complete one revolution of the black spot when a single "stopped" image is seen.

Correctly "stop" the black spot in one position only (2 slits open). Have your partner measure the time it takes you to complete 10 revolutions of the stroboscope. How many revolutions of the black spot are taking place in this time? Calculate the time for one rotation of the black spot.

5. The instructor will now increase the rate of rotation of the black spot. Remove the tape from 3 equally spaced slits, and "stop" the rotation of the black spot in one position. Calculate the time for 20 rotations of the stroboscope and from this, the time for one rotation. Repeat the above procedure with 4 equally spaced slits. (Do not change the frequency of the black spot.)

| Number of slits open | STROBOSCOPE | | | Black spot frequency (rev/sec) |
	Time for 20 revolutions (sec)	Frequency (rev/sec)	Time for 1 revolution (sec)	
3				
4				

Compare the values obtained for the frequency of the black spot when using the stroboscope with 3 and 4 open slits. How should they compare?

6. An object is vibrating with a frequency of 180 vibrations per second. You view it through a rotating 12-slit hand stroboscope.
(a) Can you "stop" its motion in one position? Discuss.

(b) Can you correctly "stop" its motion in one position? Discuss.

Expt. #2   MEASURING FREQUENCY USING THE STROBOSCOPE

Introduction In the preceding experiment we studied how the stroboscope can be used to extend our ability to measure time. In this experiment the stroboscope is actually used to determine the frequency of a bell clapper. An experimental cross-check is then performed to test our ability to use the stroboscope.

Purpose A To measure short time intervals using a stroboscope.

Apparatus

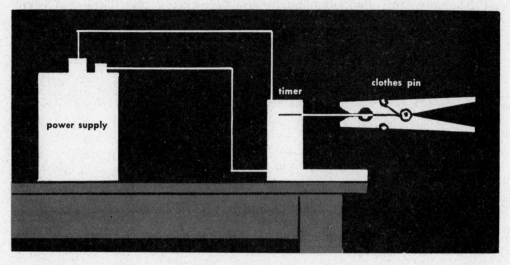

Method 1. Attach a clothes pin to the vibrator of an electric timer. This will decrease the frequency to a range which is easier to determine using the hand stroboscope. "Stop" the motion of the clothes pin by using a hand stroboscope with 4 equally spaced slits. If this is too difficult, use 6 open slits. Determine the time for one vibration of the loaded vibrator. Show all calculations below. How can you be sure you have matched the look frequency through the stroboscope with the frequency of the loaded vibrator?

2. Remove the clothes pin and find the time of one vibration of the electric timer by using 6 or 12 open slits. Calculate both the period and frequency of the clapper, showing your work below.

To cross-check the frequency for the unweighted electric timer, as determined using the stroboscope.

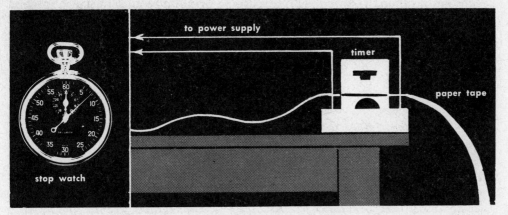

1. One student must hold the stop watch with one hand and with the other control the switch to the electric timer. The second student pulls the paper tape between the vibrator and the base. As the paper is pulled through, the vibrator will make marks at equal "time" intervals. It may be helpful to draw lines across the tape close to each end. The stop watch can then be started as the first line passes beneath the vibrator and stopped when the other line reaches it. Try several practice runs to make sure the vibrator is marking the paper tape and to determine how fast to pull the paper tape to have the marks sufficiently spaced.

2. Use this procedure to determine the frequency and period of the electric timer. Indicate clearly both the measurements taken and the calculations made.

How do these values agree with the values obtained for the unweighted electric timer using the stroboscope? Account for any differences.

3. A paper tape is pulled through beneath a vibrating bell clapper for 5 seconds, producing 120 marks, not including the first mark. The clapper's motion is then "stopped" at one extreme position by turning a stroboscope uniformly through 21 revolutions in 7 seconds. How many open slits does the stroboscope have? Show your calculations.

~~~~~~

Expt. #3   MEASURING SMALL DISTANCES—AN INDIRECT METHOD

Introduction   The optical micrometer shown below enables one to measure very small distances, such as the thickness of a razor blade, which cannot be measured accurately with a ruler. The use of this instrument will be studied in this experiment.

Purpose   To study the use of the optical micrometer in measuring small distances.

Apparatus

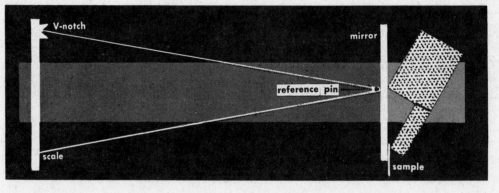

Method   1. Arrange the apparatus as in the diagram, with the uncemented mirror held by the clip which is next to the metal fulcrum. Through the V-notch you should see the image of the scale in the middle of the mirror.

2. Locate the mirror support bracket. By moving the pointer arm, adjust the mirror so that the support bracket lines up with the #1 on the scale. Insert a piece of paper between the mirror and the metal fulcrum (as shown) and note the scale reading. Is the distance between the two scale readings larger or smaller than the thickness of the paper?

3. You will now experimentally find the relationship between the optical micrometer reading and the sample thickness by placing single sheets of paper from a writing pad, whose thickness you can calculate, between the mirror and the glass plate. Measure, using a ruler, the thickness of the writing pad in centimeters (cm). Count the number of sheets and from this calculate the thickness of each sheet.

What assumption do you make in finding the thickness of one sheet by this procedure?

This method of finding the thickness is called an *indirect* method. When using a procedure such as this, a cross-check should always be performed if possible. Using a micrometer screw gauge, measure the thickness of the pad and again calculate the thickness of one sheet.

Which method is more accurate? What source of error is present, particularly when using a micrometer screw gauge?

4. To calibrate the micrometer, insert sheets of paper (first one, then two, etc.) between the mirror and the glass plate until a total of 10 sheets are present. Note the scale reading in each case and fill in the following chart.

Total number of sheets	Initial scale reading	Final scale reading	Number of divisions moved
0			
1			
2			
3			
4			
5			
6			
7			
8			
9			
10			

5. (a) Plot a graph of the total number of divisions moved with reference to the start against the number of paper sheets inserted. Describe the graph. Compare the number of scale divisions moved when one sheet, and then two sheets, are inserted.

   (b) Using your results from the above table, calculate the average number of divisions moved per sheet. Show the calculations below.

   (c) What property of the graph plotted in 5 (a) will give you the average number of divisions moved per sheet? Using this property, determine the average number of divisions moved per sheet.

   (d) Compare the value obtained from the graph in 5 (c) with that calculated in 5 (b) by determining the percentage difference between the readings. Assume that the result from the graph is the correct value.

6. Using the results of 3 and 5 (c), calibrate the scale on the micrometer in cm, correct to four decimal places.

7. Determine the thickness of each of the following samples by using the optical micrometer. Record the results in the chart.

Object	Thickness in scale divisions	Thickness in centimeters
Garbage bag		
Paper tissue (double thickness)		
Foolscap paper		
Aluminum foil		
Cardboard		
Human hair		
Razor blade		

8. Make two parallel cuts very close together on a piece of paper by moving two razor blades held side by side across the page. Sketch the end view of the razor blades, with the straight edge down, as seen through a hand lens. Explain how the optical micrometer can be used to determine the distance between the cuts, including any assumptions that are involved in using this procedure. Find this distance correct to four decimal places and enter in the chart.

MEASURING LARGE DISTANCES—AN INDIRECT METHOD Expt. #4

Introduction

Very large distances, such as the height of a mountain or the distance to a star, cannot be measured using a ruler or other standard measuring device. An indirect method can be used, however, based on the geometry of similar triangles and called "triangulation."

Purpose

To use an indirect method (triangulation) to measure a large distance and to cross-check this using a direct method (tape measure).

Apparatus

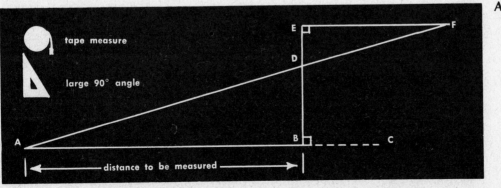

Method

1. Five equal-sized stakes should be set up at the positions *B, C, D, E* and *F*, indicated on the diagram.

   (a) Line up stakes *B* and *C*, with a distant point *A*. Stakes *B* and *C* should be separated by about 1 m.

   (b) Construct a perpendicular at *B* using a large 90° angle, and extend this a distance of about 20 m from the stake to *D*. Place another stake *E* an additional 0.5 m from *D* and in line with *B* and *D*.

   (c) Construct a perpendicular to *BE* at *E* and extend it to *F*. Adjust the position of the stake *F* until it is in line with *AD*, but still along the perpendicular to *BE*.

   (d) Prove, by referring to the diagram, that △ *ABD* is similar to △ *DEF*. By using these similar triangles and carefully measuring the distances *BD*, *EF* and *DE*, determine the distance to point *A*.

2. Measure the distance *AB* as accurately as possible using a tape measure. Record the values obtained using the direct and indirect methods.

   Triangulation value = _____

   Measured value = _____

   Calculate the per cent error encountered when using the indirect method of triangulation. Assume the measured value is correct.

   Why is the method of triangulation called an indirect method? List several sources of error encountered. Suggest a way of minimizing each error.

3. The line *BD* is called the "base line" for this method of measurement. By comparing the distance measured in this experiment to the base line used, calculate the length of base line required to measure a distance of 10^9 m. Show your calculations. This is the distance to the moon to an order of magnitude.

4. What is the maximum base line that can be used while on the earth in measuring large distances? In order to measure the distance to far stars, suggest a way of achieving a larger base line.

Variables, Functions and Graphs

The physicist makes extensive use of mathematical tools such as functions and graphs to establish a relationship between two or more physical quantities.

The variables are first studied by performing experiments in which quantitative measurements are made. These are organized into a tabular form, but this usually, by itself, does not indicate the relationship between the variables.

Using the data, a graph is then constructed by plotting the dependent variable on the *y* axis and the independent variable on the *x* axis. If a straight-line graph results, passing through the origin, the experimenter knows that the quantity plotted on the *y* axis is directly proportional to the quantity plotted on the *x* axis. The first graph plotted is seldom a straight line, but its shape suggests the relationship that may exist. With this in mind, the data is rearranged. For example, the values for the independent variable may be squared, cubed, inverted, or square-rooted. The dependent variable is then plotted against these new values. Once the experimenter achieves a straight-line graph through the origin, he realizes that a direct proportionality exists between the variable plotted on the *y* axis and the variable plotted on the *x* axis.

The slope of any straight line is constant. The constant obtained by calculating the slope enables the experimenter to write a mathematical equation which expresses in a very concise form the relationship between the plotted variables. This equation has immense value, enabling the experimenter to predict the value of one of the variables if the other variables are given new values between those originally measured. The equation can even be used to predict results outside the limits of the original data. This can, however, lead to difficulties as you will see later.

The experiments in this lab manual make use of graphical techniques where possible. Graphs are one of the most useful tools of science, and must be mastered.

Expt. #5   HOOKE'S LAW APPLIED TO A METER STICK

Purpose   To determine the relationship between the vertical depression of the free end of a meter stick and the weight attached.

Apparatus

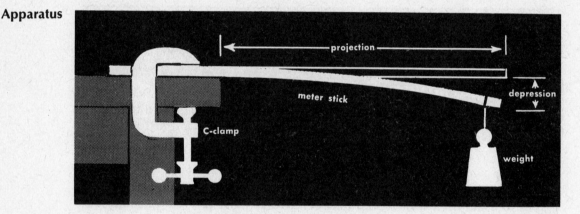

Method   1. Clamp a meter stick horizontally so that 80 cm of it projects beyond the lab table. Measure the vertical height of the free end from the floor and record in the table provided.

2. Attach a 200 gram (g) weight to the free end of the meter stick. Gently lower this weight until the meter stick supports it. Measure the vertical height of the free end from the floor and record.

3. Add weights to the free end in steps of 200 g up to a maximum amount of 1000 g. Each time a weight is added, gently lower the free end to its rest position and record the vertical height from the floor.

4. Determine the vertical depression (y) of the free end from the zero load position under the influence of the various weights. Enter these values in the table.

Weight attached w (g)	Height from floor h (cm)	Vertical depression y (cm)
0		
200		
400		
600		
800		
1000		

5. Plot a graph of vertical depression (y) against attached weight (w). Describe the graph obtained. What relationship exists between the vertical depression (y) and the weight attached (w)?

6. From the graph, determine the vertical depression when a weight of 850 g is attached. What is this graphical procedure called?

7. Determine the slope of the line of best fit from the graph and write the equation for the relationship between vertical depression and weight attached.

8. Using the equation, determine the vertical depression when a weight of 850 g is used. Show the calculations.

9. How does the value obtained in 6 compare with that obtained in 8? Which is the more accurate method? Discuss.

10. By using the equation, determine the vertical depression when a weight of 5.5 kilograms (kg) is used. Do you think this answer is valid? Explain.

What would you have to do in order to find the answer using the graph? What is this procedure called? What assumptions would be necessary?

~~~~~~

Expt. #6   THE SIMPLE BALANCE

Purpose   To describe the operation of a simple balance in terms of the relationship between the weight attached and its distance from the fulcrum.

Apparatus

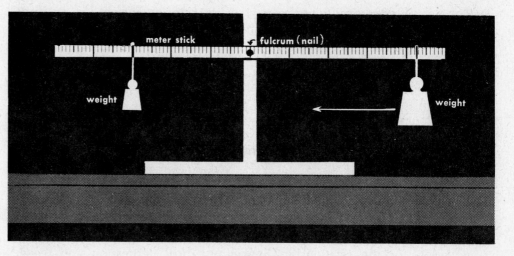

Method

1. Drill a small hole in the center of a meter stick. Balance the meter stick from a nail clamped to the retort stand as indicated in the diagram.

2. Suspend a 500 g weight by a string from the 20 cm mark on the meter stick. Suspend a 1500 g weight (w) from the opposite end, moving it along the meter stick until balance is achieved. Measure the distance of this weight from the fulcrum and record.

3. Leave the 500 g weight at the same 20 cm position and repeat the procedure using weights of 700 g, 600 g, 500 g, 400 g, and 320 g respectively. Measure the distance of the various weights from the fulcrum when balance is achieved and record.

Weight w (g)	Distance from fulcrum d (cm)		
1500			
700			
600			
500			
400			
320			

4. Plot a graph of the weights attached to produce balance (w) against their distance from the fulcrum (d). Describe the shape of the graph. When the weight was divided by 3, by what factor did the distance from the fulcrum change? What relationship exists between w and d?

5. Calculate the values of l/*distance* corresponding to each of the distance readings. Enter these in one of the blank columns of the table. Plot a graph of load (w) against l/*distance* (d^{-1}). Describe the graph. What relationship exists between the weight (w) and the distance (d)?

   Determine the slope of the line of best fit. Include units. What does this slope represent? Write the equation describing the relationship between attached weight (w) and distance from the fulcrum (d).

6. Calculate the values for the product of weight (w) and distance (d) corresponding to each measurement, and enter these in the table. Compare the product values with the slope obtained in 5. What conclusion do you make?

7. The product of the balancing weight used and its distance from the fulcrum is 500 g × 30 cm = 15000 g-cm = 1.5×10^4 g-cm. How does this compare to the values in 6?

8. A uniform beam of length 20 m is pivoting on a fulcrum located at its center. A 100 kg man wishes to teeter-totter with his son. If the son weighs 24 kg and is sitting at the end of the teeter-totter, where should the man sit with reference to the fulcrum? Show the calculations.

Expt. #7   THE SIMPLE PENDULUM

Purpose   To determine the relationship between the length and frequency of a simple pendulum.

Apparatus

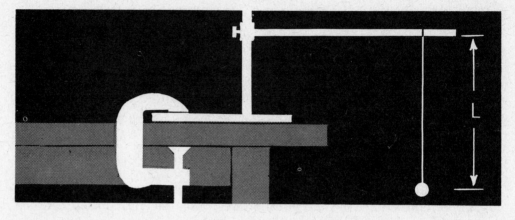

Method   1. Attach a simple pendulum to a rigid support with the center of the bob about 100 cm below the pivot point. Measure the length of the pendulum from the pivot point to the center of the bob. Pull the bob aside about 20° and release it. Using a stop watch, determine the length of time in seconds required for 30 vibrations. Record all information in the table provided.

2. Decrease the length of the pendulum from 100 cm in steps of approximately 20 cm to a final length of about 20 cm. Determine the frequency of the pendulum in vib/sec corresponding to each length and enter in the table.

Time for 30 vibrations (sec)	Pendulum frequency f (vib/sec)	Pendulum length L (cm)		

3. Plot a graph of pendulum frequency (f) against pendulum length (L). Describe the graph obtained. What happens to the frequency of the pendulum as the length is decreased? What relationship does this suggest might exist between f and L?

4. Replot the data in a form you expect will result in a straight line. Space is provided in the table for any calculations you think necessary. During the replotting of the data it may be helpful to rotate the graph paper through 90°, first looking at f as a function of L and then at L as a function of f. When a straight line graph is finally obtained, write the proportionality statement.

5. Determine the value of the proportionality constant needed to make an equation and write the equation describing:

(a) frequency and pendulum length

(b) period and pendulum length

6. Using the equation, determine the frequency of an identical pendulum of length 140 cm. Show the calculations.

7. Do you think the amplitude of the pendulum's vibration has any effect on its frequency? Discuss. Describe briefly an experiment you might perform to test your prediction. Perform it if you have time.

Expt. #8   THE PROJECTING BEAM

Purpose   To determine the relationship describing the effect of meter-stick projection (L) on the vertical depression (y) of the free end.

Apparatus   As in Experiment 5.

Method   1. Clamp a meter stick horizontally so that the first 20 cm project beyond the lab table. Measure the vertical height of the free end above the floor under zero load. Record in the table.

2. Attach a 1 kg load to the free end. Measure the vertical height of the free end from the floor and record.

3. Repeat the above procedure for projections (L) in steps of 10 cm up to a maximum projection of 80 cm, maintaining the constant load of 1 kg. Measure the vertical height of the free end above the floor at each projection, each time checking the zero load height.

4. Determine the vertical depression (y) corresponding to each projection (L) and record.

Projection L (cm)	Zero load height (cm)	Load height (cm)	Vertical depression y (cm)		
0					
20					
30					
40					
50					
60					
70					
80					

5. Plot a graph of vertical depression (y) against the meter-stick projection (L). Describe the graph obtained. What change do you think should be made in the data to produce a straight line when replotted?

6. Replot the data in the form you think will result in a straight line. Tables are provided for any calculations you think necessary. You may have to replot the data a number of times.

When a straight-line graph is finally obtained, write the proportionality statement and, by using the graph, determine the proportionality constant.

Write the equation describing the relationship between vertical depression (y) and projection (L) for a constant load of 1 kg.

7. A meter stick has a load of 1 kg attached to its free end, which projects 42 cm beyond a lab table. Using the equation, determine the vertical depression which this meter stick will experience. Show all calculations.

8. Do you think the cross-sectional area of a beam has any effect on the vertical depression at a given extension? Discuss. Describe an experiment you might perform to test your prediction. Perform it if you have time.

9. A diving board has a vertical depression of 6 inches when a 100-pound man stands 8 feet from the fulcrum. Determine the weight of a man who causes the same diving board to deflect 4 inches vertically when he stands 6 feet from the fulcrum. Show your reasoning and complete solution.

Expt. #9   ANALYSIS OF DATA

Introduction   An experiment was performed to study the relationship between the frequency and diameter and the frequency and tension of wires of constant length and density. To find the dependence on the diameter of the wire, different diameter wires were attached to a rigid support and aligned horizontally with the free end hanging over a pulley. They were placed under the same tension by attaching the same amount of mass (C-clamps) to the end passing over the pulley. To find the dependence on tension, the experiment was repeated for the different diameter wires with different masses attached to the free end.

The wires were vibrated and the frequency was determined using a stroboscope for each condition of diameter and tension.

By repeating all measurements a number of times, an average frequency corresponding to each set of conditions has been entered in the table below. The data in the table can be analyzed using graphical techniques to establish the relationship between the frequency (f), diameter of the wire (d), and the tension in the wire (T).

Purpose   To analyze an experiment using a graphical method and discover mathematical relationships to describe the results.

Information

Rearranged diameter	T (C-clamps) / d (cm)	Frequency f (vib/sec)			
		3	5	8	14
	.25	83	108	135	180
	.15	138	179	226	299
	.06	347	448	555	750
	.01	2080	2700	3390	4480

Method   1. On graph paper #1 plot frequency (f) in vib/sec versus the diameter (d) in cm of the wire for a constant tension (T) of 3 C-clamps. Use one sheet of graph paper and, to obtain maximum accuracy, plot the data across the whole sheet.

From your graph predict the frequency a wire of diameter .10 cm would have with 3 C-clamps attached. What name is given to this method of using the graph?

What graphical procedure would be necessary to predict the above if the diameter of the wire was .5 cm? How accurate do you think the result would be? Why? Discuss.

By examining the graph, what happens to the value of f as d is increased? What kind of relationship does this suggest?

If the value of d is doubled, what happens to the value of f (tension remaining constant)?

2. Rearrange the data for the diameter in such a manner as you think will result in a straight line when plotted. Use the space provided in the information table to record your figures. Plot this data on graph paper #2. Space the frequency axis so that the maximum frequency for the other tensions can be plotted on this graph later.

When a straight line graph is obtained, describe the relationship between frequency of the wire under a constant tension, and the diameter of the wire?

Express this as an equation and calculate the value of the constant by referring to the graph.

Using this equation, determine the frequency of a wire made of the same material under a tension of 3 C-clamps, but having a diameter of .10 cm. Which is the more accurate method of determining the result—from graph #1, or from the equation? Why?

3. In order to determine if the same relationship between f and d holds when the wires are placed under different tensions, plot the data of f against $1/d$

for the other tensions on graph #2. Label each curve as to the tension plotted. Describe the resulting graph. What effect does tension have on the relationship between *f* and *d*? Discuss.

4. On graph paper #3, plot *f* on the vertical axis and *T* on the horizontal axis for a constant diameter of 0.25 cm, in order to determine the relationship between frequency and tension. Join the points with a smooth line. If the trend of the line is maintained, does it pass through the origin? Should it? Discuss.

Examine this curve visually and try to guess the correct mathematical relationship between *f* and *T*. What do you think it is? Give your reasons.

5. Plot on graph #4 f^2 versus *T* for a constant diameter of 0.25 cm. Fill in the following table before plotting the graph.

T (C-clamps)	f^2 (vib^2/sec^2)	*f* (vib/sec)
3		83
5		108
8		135
14		180

What kind of graph do you get on plotting this data?

How does f^2 vary with *T*?

How must *f* vary with *T*?

Check to see if the same kind of relationship between *f* and *T* holds for *d* = 0.06 cm. Does it? How did you check?

6. A simple way to check if the relationship between *f* and *T* follows the pattern of $f \propto T^n$ is to plot log *f* against log *T* on linear graph paper, or *f* versus *T* on log-log graph paper.

Plot graph #5 using either of these methods and describe the resulting graph.

What is the value of the slope of this graph? What is the value of *n* in the expression $f \propto T^n$?

7. We shall make use of graphs #3 and #2 in two ways to find the frequency (*f*) for which *d* = .04 cm and *T* = 12 C-clamps.

(a) Using graph #3, interpolate the value of *f* when *T* = 12 C-clamps and *d* = .25 cm. What value do you get in vib/sec?

_____ vib/sec

Since we have established *f* = *K* 1/*d*, where *K* is the proportionality constant, we can mark the frequency *f* found above at *d* = .25 cm (1/*d* = 1/.25 = 4.0) on graph #2 and draw a straight line through the origin. On this line read the value of *f* for 1/*d* = 1/.04 = 25. Tabulate the value you obtain below.

f = _____ vib/sec

(b) Using graph #2, read the values of *f* by interpolation for all the four values of tension plotted for 1/*d* = 1/.04 = 25. Complete the table below.

d (cm)	*T* (C-clamps)	*f* (vib/sec)
.04	3	
.04	5	
.04	8	
.04	14	

Using linear graph paper (#6), plot *f* (vib/sec) on the vertical axis versus *T* (C-clamps) on the horizontal axis for a constant diameter of .04 cm. From this graph, by interpolation, find the value of *f* for *T* = 12 C-clamps. Tabulate below.

f = _____ vib/sec

8. From graphs #2 and #4, what is the proportionality statement for f as a function of both T and d?

Express this as a general equation and calculate the value of the proportionality constant by taking the most accurate values from the experiment for frequency, diameter, and tension. What value do you obtain for the constant? Include units.

constant = _____

Using the equation, calculate f for d = .04 cm and T = 12 C-clamps. Compare the answer with that found graphically in Part 7. Which procedure do you think is more accurate? Discuss.

9. When a wire, the same length as those used in the experiment but of diameter .20 cm, is placed under a tension of 20 C-clamps, it vibrates with a frequency of 358 vib/sec. Another wire made of the same material and having the same length has a frequency of 716 vib/sec when 18 C-clamps are attached.

(a) What is the new diameter of the wire used? Show all calculations.

(b) Are the wires in this problem made of the same material as those used in the experiment? Give your reasons.

10. Do you think the density of the material making up the wire or the length of the wire has any affect on its frequency? If so, how do you think each would affect it? If you have time, perform an experiment to test your predictions. Summarize the procedure used below.

Motion Along a Straight Line

POSITION, VELOCITY AND ACCELERATION **Expt. #10**

Introduction

A thorough understanding of the meaning of the terms position, displacement, velocity and acceleration is essential to the study of motion. Graphical techniques play a major role in the study of mechanics. The following experiments will make extensive use of graphs in the study of the motion of objects along a straight line path.

Purpose

To describe the motion of an object by using position-time and velocity-time graphs.

Apparatus

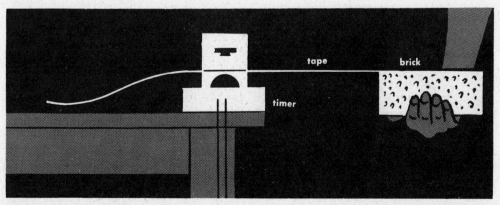

1. Set up the timer as shown and adjust the clapper to a specific rate by connecting it to a 1.5 volt DC source.

2. With masking tape, attach a 1.5 m length of paper tape to a brick. Grasp the brick and move your hand steadily, pulling the tape at a uniform rate through the clapper.

3. Label the first mark "starting point" ($t = 0$) and mark the tape off into 10-tick intervals called "tocks." Number these 1, 2, 3, etc.

4. Measure the distance from each tenth dot (tock) to the starting point ($t = 0$). Tabulate this in the position column.

5. Measure the displacement (change in position) in *each* tock interval and tabulate in the displacement column.

6. Calculate the average velocity during each tock interval and tabulate.

Time T (tock)	Position (from start) $\overrightarrow{x}$ (cm)	Displacement $\overrightarrow{d}$ (cm)	Average velocity $\overrightarrow{V_{av}}$ (cm/tock)
1			
2			
3			
4			
5			
6			
7			
8			
9			
10			
11			

7. Plot a position-time graph (using the tock as the unit of time) on the upper half of one sheet of graph paper. By referring to the graph, describe the type of motion the brick was undergoing. What does the slope of this graph represent?

8. Plot an average velocity-time graph on the lower half of the graph paper using the values calculated in the table. Describe the graph. Was the average velocity constant? Discuss.

9. By using measurements taken from the tape, calculate the average velocity for the total journey of the brick. Describe the procedure used. Compare the average velocity for the total journey with the average velocities for intermediate stages of the trip plotted on the graph.

~~~~~~ ●

UNIFORM ACCELERATION Expt. #11

Introduction

In the last experiment we studied graphs of an object under uniform motion. In this experiment we will study a more complex motion—accelerated motion.

Purpose

To study the accelerated motion of an object.

Apparatus

Method

1. Set up an inclined plane about 2 m long, with one end approximately 0.25 m higher than the other. Clamp a timer to the raised end in such a position that the tape can be pulled through the timer down the length of the plane. Attach a 2 m length of tape to a cart loaded with 2 bricks. Thread this tape through the timer until the timer is almost touching the cart. One student must be at the lower end of the inclined plane to catch the cart. Activate the timer and release the cart. Repeat until each student in the group has one tape.

2. Label the first mark made "starting point" ($t = 0$) and mark the tape off into 5-tick time intervals called "picks." Number these 1, 2, 3, etc. Be sure to include the closely spaced dots at the start.

3. Tabulate the position from the start in cm corresponding to each pick in the table.

4. Measure the displacement (change in position) during each pick interval and tabulate in the displacement column.

5. Calculate the average velocity during each pick interval and record.

Time T (pick)	Position (from start) $\vec{x}$ (cm)	Displacement $\vec{d}$ (cm)	Average velocity $\vec{V}_{av}$ (cm/pick)	Instantaneous velocity (from tangents) $\vec{V}$ (cm/pick)
1				
2				
3				
4				
5				
6				
7				
8				
9				
10				
11				
12				
13				
14				
15				

6. Plot a position-time graph of this data making maximum use of one sheet of graph paper. Describe the graph. What type of motion was the object undergoing? Why?

Calculate the instantaneous velocity at $1/2$-pick intervals ($1/2$, $1 1/2$, $2 1/2$, etc.), by constructing tangents at $1/2$-pick intervals. Tabulate the values in the table. How do these values compare with the average velocities for each pick interval? What conclusion can you draw?

7. (a) Plot a velocity-time graph using the average velocities calculated, but plot at $1/2$ pick. Why? Describe the graph. What type of acceleration did the cart have?

(b) Calculate the area beneath the velocity-time graph. Show the calculations below. Compare this area with the displacement measured on the tape from $t = 0$ up to the last pick plotted. What conclusion can you draw?

(c) Calculate the average acceleration of the cart in cm/pick^2 for two different pick intervals by measuring slopes from the graph. Show the calculations below. What kind of acceleration does the cart have? Plot an acceleration-time graph. Describe the graph.

8. Given that the frequency of the clapper is 40 vps, calculate:

(a) the period of the clapper

(b) the average acceleration of the cart in cm/sec^2

Expt. #12   NON-UNIFORM ACCELERATION

Introduction   How are velocity, displacement and acceleration interrelated when the velocity changes with time in a non-uniform way? An automobile which increases velocity and then slows down for a stop light illustrates the type of motion to be studied in this experiment.

Purpose   To study non-uniformly accelerated motion.

Apparatus

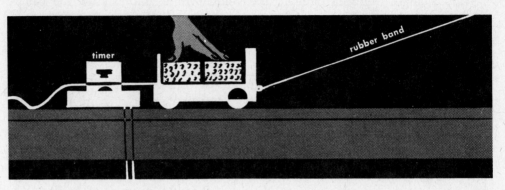

Method

1. Thread a 1.5 m length of paper tape through the timer and attach it to a cart loaded with 2 bricks.

2. Attach a looped rubber band to the cart. While holding the cart rigid, stretch the rubber band about halfway down the lab table holding it at a fixed position about 0.25 m above the table.

3. Activate the timer and release the cart. Attempt to describe the type of motion the cart is undergoing before you begin analyzing the tape.

4. Divide the paper tape into pick intervals. Measure the displacement in each pick interval and record. From this calculate the average velocity during each pick.

5. Plot a velocity-time graph by plotting the average velocity at $\frac{1}{2}$-pick ($\frac{1}{2}$, $1\frac{1}{2}$, $2\frac{1}{2}$) intervals. Describe the graph. For how long was the velocity increasing?

6. Calculate the change in velocity during each 1-pick interval and hence the average acceleration during this interval. Plot an acceleration-time graph. Describe the graph. For how long was the acceleration of the cart positive?

38

Time T (pick)	Displacement $\vec{d}$ (cm)	Average velocity $\vec{V}_{av}$	Change in velocity $\Delta\vec{V}$ (cm/pick)	Acceleration $\vec{a}$ (cm/pick²)
1				
2				
3				
4				
5				
6				
7				
8				
9				
10				
11				
12				
13				
14				
15				

7. Explain how the instantaneous acceleration at time 4 picks can be obtained from the velocity-time graph.

8. By using the velocity-time graph, determine the average positive acceleration and the average negative acceleration. Show the calculations below.

9. Calculate the area under the velocity-time graph from the starting point to various subsequent times. Plot a position-time graph with the same time axis as the other two graphs. Compare the total displacement of the cart, found by calculating the area underneath the velocity-time graph, with the length measured from the tape.

Describe clearly a method of obtaining the velocity- and acceleration-time graphs from the position-time graph.

Describe clearly a method of obtaining the velocity- and position-time graphs from the acceleration-time graph.

10. The rate of change of acceleration is called "jerk" motion. Sketch a jerk-time graph for the cart's motion.

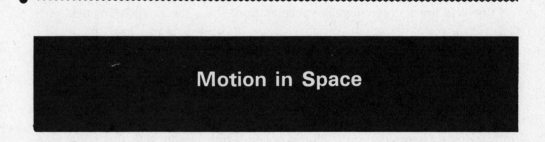

Motion in Space

Expt. #13   ACCELERATION AS A VECTOR

Introduction When studying the motion of bodies in space, it is often useful to resolve a vector into components in a chosen direction. Any vector quantity can be resolved into components. This will provide us with a simple test for the vector nature of a quantity. It is, however, not a complete test.

40 **Purpose** To test the vector nature of acceleration.

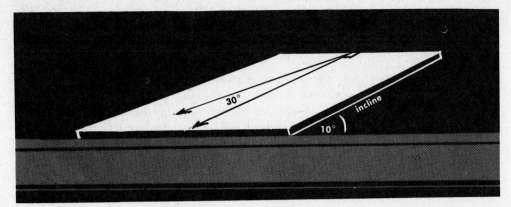

1. Set up an inclined plane with a large surface area at an angle of about 10° to the horizontal. Roll a cart loaded with 2 bricks straight down the incline and observe its acceleration. Roll the loaded cart down the incline at various angles to the original direction and describe the variation of acceleration with the angle.

2. Attach a paper tape to the cart, activate the timer, and roll the cart straight down the incline. Mark this tape a_s.

3. Mark off a path at 30° to the previous direction. Attach a paper tape to the cart, activate the timer, and roll it down this path. Mark this tape $a\angle$.

From the previous inclined plane experiment, we know the acceleration of the cart on the incline is constant in a given direction. In order to compare the accelerations, it is not necessary to calculate the acceleration for more than one time interval on each tape.

Consider a body starting from *rest* with a constant acceleration (a). In a time (t), it moves a distance (d), given by $d = \frac{1}{2}at^2$. Hence $a = 2d/t^2$. If the two runs to be considered extend over the same time, the acceleration in each case is proportional to the distance moved. Therefore:

$$a_s = \frac{2d_s}{t_s^2} \text{ and } a\angle = \frac{2d\angle}{t\angle^2}, \text{ but if } t_s = t\angle, \text{ therefore } t_s^2 = t\angle^2,$$

$$\text{therefore } \frac{a_s}{a\angle} = \frac{d_s}{d\angle}, \text{ or } a \propto d.$$

We can compare accelerations in the different directions by comparing the distance travelled in each direction starting from rest in the *same time interval*.

6. Count off the number of ticks starting from rest on the $a\angle$ tape corresponding to the time when the cart was accelerating. Count off the same number of ticks on the a_s tape. You may find it difficult to resolve the dots on the tape at the beginning of the run. It is important to estimate them as accurately as possible, however.

7. Measure the displacement corresponding to this time on each tape. Starting from the same point, using a suitable scale, draw acceleration vectors at 30° to each other, corresponding to these displacement vectors.

8. Resolve the straight-down acceleration vector a_s to find its component at 30°. How does this component compare with the measured vector representing the acceleration at 30° to straight down the incline? By what percentage does it differ from the measured acceleration? Is this a significant difference? Discuss.

•

Unit II

•

OPTICS
AND
WAVES

~~~~~~

How Light Behaves

The Particle Model of Light

Waves Propagated in One Dimension

Waves Propagated in Two Dimensions

Interference

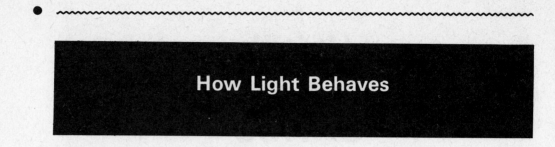

How Light Behaves

Expt. #14   PLANE MIRRORS, REFLECTION AND PARALLAX

Introduction   Non-luminous objects, such as baseballs, are seen by the light they reflect. Because the eye detects the light coming from the object rather than the object itself, the object may appear to be at one location and yet really be at another. It is important to know something about the reflection of light in order to understand some common phenomena.

Purpose   To study parallax and light reflection.

Apparatus

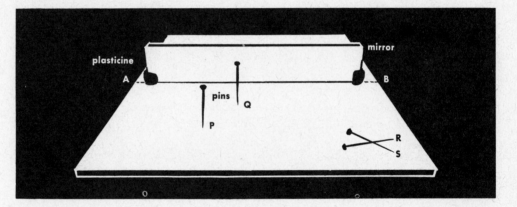

Method   1. (a) Point the thumb of one hand upward at arm's length. Point the thumb of the other hand upward halfway between the far thumb and your eye. Move your head until the thumbs and your eye are along one straight line.

   (b) Keeping your thumbs stationary, view them from different positions by moving your head first to one side and then the other. In which direction does the closer thumb seem to move in relation to the other as your head moves from left to right?

   (c) Decrease the distance between the thumbs and repeat the procedure. As the thumbs are brought closer together describe the apparent change in their positions using the same amount of head motion as above.

In what position is it necessary to place the thumbs with reference to one another to make them appear motionless when viewed from different angles?

What is "parallax"?

You are driving across the Prairies on the Trans-Canada Highway when you see two grain combines off to your left in the distance. One is red, the other green. At one instant the red combine appears to be to the left of the green one. A short time later their apparent positions are reversed. Are the combines moving? Discuss.

2. We will study reflection by sighting rays.

(a) Place a sheet of paper on a tack board; draw a horizontal line *AB* midway across the page. Support the plane mirror perpendicular to the page with its back edge along the line *AB*.

(b) Place pins *P* and *Q* about 5 cm apart so that the line joining *P* and *Q* strikes the mirror obliquely.

(c) Look into the mirror with one eye at the level of the paper and line up the images of *P* and *Q*. Insert pins *R* and *S* in line with these images.

(d) Mark the position of all pins. Remove the mirror and pins. Draw lines *PQ* and *RS* extending them to meet at *O*. Draw *NO* perpendicular to *AB*. With a protractor, measure angles *PON* and *SON*. Record in the table.

(e) Repeat steps *b, c* and *d*, with pins *P* and *Q* in other positions twice more. Record all values in the table.

	Angle of incidence	Angle of reflection
1		
2		
3		

How does the angle of incidence compare with the angle of reflection?

State the Laws of Reflection. (Refer to your text if necessary.)

(i)

(ii)

Draw a diagram and label: incident ray, reflected ray, point of incidence, normal, angle of incidence, angle of reflection, reflecting surface.

Draw another diagram of an object in the shape of an erect half arrow in front of a mirror. Place an observer's eye on the diagram and trace with arrowheads the path the rays take on being reflected to reach the eye, thereby showing how the eye sees the object. Use two rays for each point considered on the object.

3. The location of an object can be determined by drawing rays to represent the direction light travels from it directly to the eye. *No mirror is necessary.* Stick an object pin vertically into a paper sitting on a tack board. Look at this pin from various directions, each time marking the direction in which light comes to your eye by sticking two additional pins into the paper between your eye and the object pin. Mark the location of all pins. Draw rays connecting the position of the object pin and these reference pins. Where do these lines intersect? What kind of pencil of light is formed by any two of these rays?

You have undoubtedly seen your image staring back at you from a plane mirror. Where is this image, what are its characteristics, and why is it there? This experiment should help you answer these questions. **Introduction**

To determine the positions and characteristics of the images formed by a plane mirror. **Purpose**

Apparatus

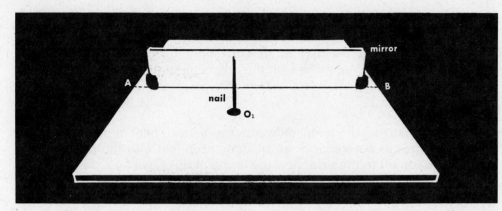

1. (a) Draw a line *AB* horizontally across the middle of a sheet of paper. Support the plane mirror vertically with its reflecting surface along the line *AB*. Stand a nail at position O_1, between your eye and the reflecting surface of the mirror. Where does the image of the nail appear to be? **Method**

   (b) Place your eye in line with the object nail and image. Which way does the object nail appear to move with respect to the image as you move your head from left to right?

   Keeping in mind the ideas of parallax, where is the image with respect to the object nail?

   (c) Place a marker nail where you think the image is. Move the marker nail until the parallax disappears between it and the object nail's image. Mark the location of the image I_1.

   (d) Position the object nail at several other locations marking them O_2, O_3, etc. Locate each image by parallax. Compare the size of the object and its image.

Where is the image of the object located with reference to the object and reflecting surface? Show by geometrical construction that this position obeys the laws of reflection.

Join the object position to its corresponding image position. What angle does this line make with the reflecting surface?

2. (a) Draw a horizontal line *AB* midway across a fresh sheet of paper. Support the mirror as before. Stick an object pin upright into the paper. From a position off to the side, view the image of this object pin. Insert 2 pins vertically in the paper in line with your eye and this image. Repeat for 2 other positions of your eye. Make sure one position is on the opposite side of the object. Trace the lines joining the pins (rays) back to their points of intersection. Where do the rays appear to come from?

(b) Draw rays from the object to the intersection of the reflected rays and the reflecting surface of the mirror. Construct normals. Compare the angles of incidence and reflection.

3. Arrange 2 plane mirrors on a sheet of polar graph paper so that an angle of 90° exists between the reflecting surfaces. Stand a nail on its head between them. Locate all the images of the nail by parallax. How many images are there? Look into the mirrors with your nose located along the bisector of the 90° angle. Wink your left eye. What do you notice?

Change the angle between the mirrors to 60°, 45° and finally to 36°, each time determining the number of images. Complete the chart.

Number of images	Angle	
	180°	
	90°	
	60°	
	45°	
	36°	

Plot a graph of number of images against the angle between the mirrors. Describe the graph. Suggest how the data could be plotted to produce a straight line.

Replot the data until a straight line graph is obtained. What kind of relationship exists between the angle and the number of images? See if you can write an equation to determine the number of images for any angle which can be divided into 180°. Account for the formation of the additional images.

~~~~~~ ●

IMAGES FORMED BY A CONCAVE MIRROR   Expt. #16

Not all mirrors are plane. In this experiment we begin the study of reflecting surfaces of various shapes.   **Introduction**

To determine the nature of the images formed by a concave mirror and a relationship describing their location.   **Purpose**

Apparatus

1. One of the specifications quoted for any curved mirror is its focal length. To find the focal length of a concave mirror, face the shiny concave side so that rays from the sun (essentially parallel) or rays from a distant light source fall on it. Using a piece of paper as a screen, locate the position where the light focuses to a point. Measure the distance from the vertex of the mirror to this point image as accurately as possible and record. This distance is the focal length.   **Method**

focal length (f) = _____ cm

2. Holding the mirror facing you, examine your image and note the size and position of the image as well as its attitude as you move the mirror progressively farther away to arm's length.

3. Mount the concave mirror at one end of the optical bench. Place a light bulb (object) at the other end. Mark the location of the focal point (F) on the optical bench. Locate the image first by parallax and then by using a paper screen. In the chart provided record the distance of the object from the focal point (So) and the distance of the image from the focal point (Si) to the nearest cm, as well as the characteristics of the image.

4. Move the light bulb to a position about ³/₄ the length of the meter stick from the mirror. Locate the image. Record So, Si, and the image characteristics.

5. Move the object to exactly 2F from the mirror and repeat the above; then move it between F and 2F and repeat.

6. Place the mirror at the 50 cm mark on the optical bench and place the light bulb between the principal focus and the mirror. Locate the image by correcting for parallax. Is it erect or inverted? How does its size compare with the size of the object? Record values for So, Si, and characteristics.

7. Place the bulb at exactly F. What do you notice?

Object location	Si	So		Characteristics of image		
				Size (compared to object)	Attitude	Kind
At end						
At ³/₄ way						
At 2F						
Between F and 2F						
At F						
Inside F						

Questions   1. What happens to Si as So increases?

2. How does the size of the image compare with the object size when the object distance (So) is:

(a) larger than the focal length?

(b) smaller than the focal length?

(c) the same as the focal length?

3. For what range of positions is the image clearly defined? Why is it impossible to obtain an image when the object is placed at the principal focus?

4. Using regular graph paper, plot Si as a function of So. Describe the graph obtained. How might the data be plotted in order to obtain a straight line?

5. Replot the data to produce a straight line. What kind of mathematical relationship exists between Si and So?

6. Using graphical techniques, determine the equation for this relationship and indicate your answer below.

7. Using this equation, determine where the object must be placed in order to obtain an image a distance of 400 cm from F. Show your complete solution.

~~~~~~ ●

LIGHT AND REFRACTION Expt. #17

In travelling from one transparent material to another transparent material, light is bent from its original path, provided it hits the interface between the two at an angle other than 90°. This is called refraction. We will be making frequent reference to the angle between a line drawn perpendicular to the surface at the point of incidence (the normal) and the incident ray. Physicists call this angle **Introduction** the angle of incidence ($\angle$ i). The angle between the normal and the refracted ray is called the angle of refraction ($\angle$ R). The diagram below should clarify the above discussion, if you label it.

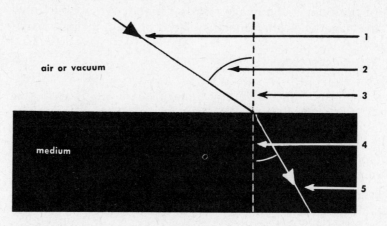

Purpose To trace the path of light through various materials and discover a relationship describing this path.

Apparatus

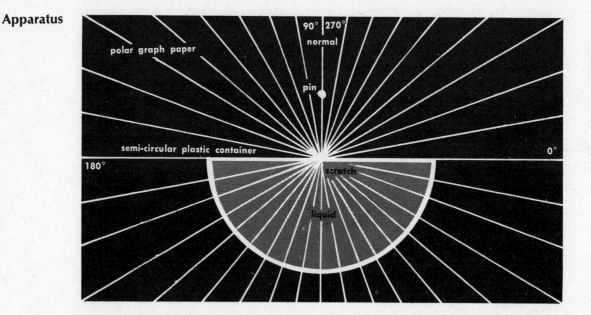

Method Examine the semicircular plastic container and locate the vertical line scratched on the flat surface. Various liquids may be used in the lab. Some of you will be using *water*; others will be using *glycerine* and *mineral oil. Do not use* carbon tetrachloride, carbon disulfide, turpentine, or acids and bases.

1. Fill the box half full of the liquid; place the polar graph paper on the tack board and align the flat surface of the dish along the 0°–180° line of the graph paper with the scratch line directly over the origin of all the lines. Insert pin *A* vertically into the paper about 4 cm from the scratch on the 90°–270° line. Consider the 90°–270° line to be the normal. Look at pin *A* through the liquid *from* the curved side and line up the scratch and pin *A*. Insert pin *B* in line with these two points. Is light refracted when incident on a

surface at a 90° angle? Does it matter whether the light is entering or leaving the liquid?

2. Position pin A at a distance no greater than 4 cm from the scratch to obtain an angle of incidence of 10° and again align the image of pin A, the scratch, and pin B. Very carefully mark the positions of these corresponding pins and repeat this for angles of incidence 20°, 30°, 40°, 50°, 60°, 70°, and 80°. Record the paired values for the angles of incidence and angles of refraction in the table provided. Read the angles of refraction to the nearest 1/10°.

3. Carefully set the plastic container aside. With a sharp pencil and a ruler, join the pinholes to the origin and extend back to cut a circle of radius 6 cm or greater. Label the positions where the line in air cuts the circle (A), and where the line in liquid cuts the circle (B). From A drop a perpendicular to the normal at E and from B drop a perpendicular to the normal at F. AE represents the semi-chord in air and BF the semi-chord in the liquid. The above construction is indicated below.

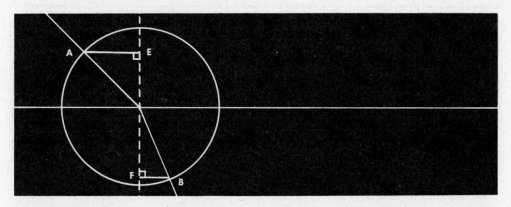

Repeat this procedure for all the other points and record all the values for AE and BF to the nearest 0.10 cm in the table.

4. With the semi-circular container on the paper, repeat the procedure for $\angle i = 30°$. Line up the pins as before by looking through from the curved side. Following this, look through the liquid from the flat side of the dish. How does the direction the light is travelling now compare with the previous direction? Does this have any effect on the path the light takes? Discuss.

5. The other student groups will give you the angle of refraction which corresponds to an angle of incidence of 30° for the various liquids used. Do different liquids cause light to refract differently?

Observations

$\angle i$	$\angle R$	sin $\angle i$	sin $\angle R$	$\angle i / \angle R$	$\dfrac{\sin \angle i}{\sin \angle R}$	AE	BF	$\dfrac{AE}{BF}$
0								
10°								
20°								
30°								
40°								
50°								
60°								
70°								
*80°								

* You may have difficulty with this value.

Calculations

1. Calculate the ratio of $\angle i / \angle R$ and plot the ratio on a graph as a function of the angle of incidence. Do you get a straight line? Discuss.

2. Calculate the ratio of *AE/BF* for each pair of rays, and plot the ratio as a function of the angle of incidence on the above graph. Which relationship more closely approaches a straight line?

3. From mathematical tables, look up the values of sin $\angle i$ and sin $\angle R$. Calculate the ratio sin $\angle i$ / sin $\angle R$ and plot this on a new sheet of graph paper as a function of $\angle i$.

4. Which of the three ratios calculated is most nearly constant? What simple mathematical relation do you think best describes the refraction of light?

54

5. What is the ratio $\dfrac{\sin \angle i}{\sin \angle R}$ or $\dfrac{AE}{BF}$ called?

6. By referring to the constructions made earlier, prove that $\sin \angle i / \sin \angle R = AE/BF$.

7. Light travelling through a transparent solid having an index of refraction (n) of 2.42 is incident on the solid-air boundary at an angle of incidence ($\angle i$) of 20°. Determine:

(a) the angle of refraction ($\angle R$)

(b) the angle of incidence ($\angle i$) necessary to obtain an $\angle R = 90°$. What is this angle called?

~~~~~~ ●

IMAGES FORMED BY A CONVERGING LENS **Expt. #18**

In the study of concave mirrors we formulated a simple mathematical relationship which enables us to determine the image position for any object position with any focal length mirror. Is there such a relationship for a lens? **Introduction**

To determine the nature of images formed by a convex lens. **Purpose**

Apparatus

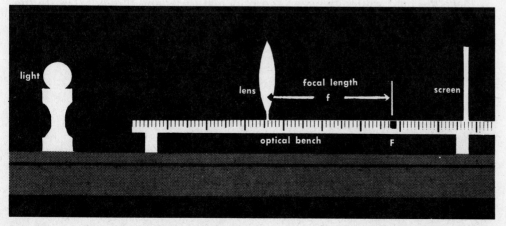

Method   1. Just as a curved mirror has a focal length and principal focus, so also does a lens. To find the focal length of a converging lens, let the rays from the sun or a distant light source (greater than 5 m) fall on the lens. Focus the light on a sheet of paper and *very accurately* measure the focal length and record.

focal length (*f*) = _____ cm

Reverse the lens and repeat the above procedure. How many principal foci does the lens have? Are they the same distance from the lens?

View an object without a convex lens and then through the lens by placing it between your eye and the object. Compare the size and attitude of the image, as viewed through the lens, with the true nature of the object.

Move the lens closer and farther away from an object. Do the size and position of the image change when the lens is moved with respect to the object?

2. Mount the lens in a holder at the center of the optical bench and place a light bulb about 1 m from the lens. Mark the location of the focal point (*F*) on the optical bench. Locate the image first by parallax and then by using a paper screen. In the chart provided, record the distance of the object from the focal point on the object side (*So*), the distance of the image from the focal point on the image side (*Si*), and the characteristics of the image.

3. Move the light bulb to the end of the optical bench. Locate the image and record *So*, *Si* and characteristics.

4. Move the light bulb to exactly *2F* from the lens and repeat the above; then between *F* and *2F* and repeat. Be sure you record *Si* and *So* in all cases.

5. Place the light source between the principal focus and the lens. Locate the image by parallax. Is it upside down or right side up? How does its size compare with the object size? Record the values of *Si* and *So* and the image characteristics.

6. Place the bulb at exactly *F*. What do you notice?

Object location	Si (cm)	So (cm)		Characteristics of image		
				Size (compared to object)	Attitude	Kind
About 1 m away						
At end						
At 2F						
Between F and 2F						
At F						
Inside F						

1. What happens to Si as So increases?

2. How does the size of the image compare with the object size when the object distance is:

   (a) larger than the focal length?

   (b) smaller than the focal length?

   (e) the same as the focal length?

3. For what range of positions can you locate the image? Why is it impossible to obtain an image when the object is placed at the principal focus?

4. Using regular graph paper, plot Si as a function of So. Describe the graph obtained. How might the data be plotted in order to obtain a straight line?

5. Replot the data to produce a straight-line graph. What kind of mathematical relationship exists between Si and So?

6. Using graphical techniques, determine the equation for this relationship. Show your work.

7. Using this equation, determine where the object must be placed in order to obtain an image a distance of 450 cm from *F*. Show your complete solution.

The Particle Model of Light

Expt. #19   SNELL'S LAW AND PARTICLE REFRACTION

Introduction   A steel ball projected along a slope changes direction and speed. If the ball is given the same speed for each trial run on the upper surface, but intercepts the slope at different oblique angles, is the path it takes on the lower surface predictable? If so, can the path be determined using Snell's Law?

Purpose   To determine if the refracting particles of a mechanical model obey Snell's Law.

Apparatus

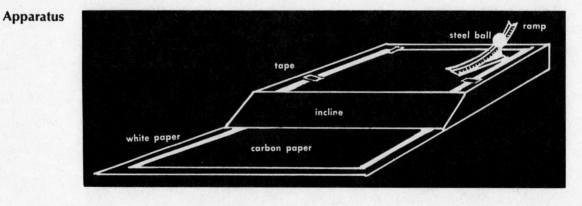

Method   1. Arrange the ramp as shown in the diagram. Place a plain sheet of paper with its edge along the edge of the slope on both the upper and lower level surfaces. Tape a sheet of carbon paper face down over each plain sheet of paper as shown.

2. Place the launching ramp about 15 cm from the slope. Release the steel ball from a point about halfway up the ramp so that it intercepts the slope at an angle of 90°. Is there any refraction? How is this setup similar to the one with light and a glass plate with parallel sides?

3. Release the steel ball from the *same point*, about halfway up the launching ramp, at different oblique angles to the slope. Label the paths made by the ball on the upper and lower surfaces for each trial run R_1, R_2, R_3, etc. The front end of the ramp should be the same distance from the point where the ball will intercept the slope each time, but try to have the ball intercept the slope at different locations.

4. Construct normals at the slope. Measure the angles of incidence and refraction corresponding to each run and record in the table provided.

Run	$\angle i$	$\angle R$	sin $\angle i$	sin $\angle R$
R_1				
R_2				
R_3				
R_4				
R_5				

5. (a) Plot a graph of sin $\angle i$ versus sin $\angle R$. Describe the graph. Determine the slope of the line of best fit showing your calculations below. To what does this slope correspond in the study of light? Do particles obey Snell's Law? Discuss.

   (b) What happens to the speed of the particles as their direction of travel bends toward the normal? According to these results, how should the speed of light in water compare to the speed in a vacuum?

6. Set up the apparatus as in Part 1. Release the steel ball from the *top* of the launching ramp to intercept the slope obliquely. Measure $\angle i$ and $\angle R$. Determine the index of refraction for this setup. How does it compare with the value obtained in 5 (a)? Explain.

7. Set up the apparatus as in Part 1, but this time place the launching ramp on the lower level. Arrange to launch the ball from a point about 3 cm higher than the upper level. Experiment to determine if particles can undergo total internal reflection with this model. If so, what is the critical angle?

Expt. #20 LIGHT INTENSITY AND DISTANCE

Introduction According to the particle model of light, the particles travelling away from a point source in a straight line spread apart, and the same number of particles passes through progressively greater and greater areas. The area through which a given number of particles passes increases as the square of the distance from the source, and the number of particles passing through a unit area therefore decreases proportional to the square of the distance.

A good test for the particle model would be to determine if the intensity of light from a point source is inversely proportional to the distance squared from the source.

Purpose To study the relationship between the intensity of light and the distance from a point source.

Apparatus

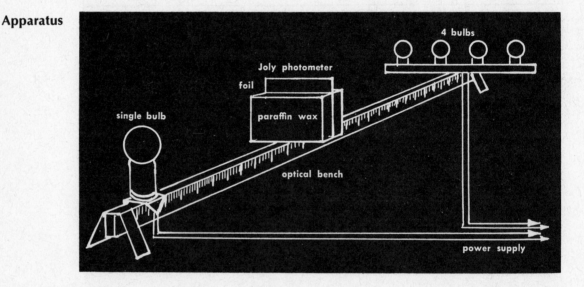

Method This experiment must be performed in a room kept as dark as possible.

1. Place the single light bulb at one end of the optical bench with its center at the 0 cm mark. Unscrew three of the four bulbs and place this fixture at the 100 cm mark. Attach the two light sources in parallel to the same 12-volt source. Adjust the Joly photometer between the light sources until the two halves are equally illuminated. Where is the Joly photometer situated?

How does the intensity of light hitting each side of the Joly photometer compare?

Compare the power of the two light bulbs. What relationship exists between intensity and the power of the light source if the distance is constant?

In the chart provided, record the distance from the single light bulb to the Joly photometer.

2. Keep the Joly photometer at the same position. Screw in one more bulb. Move the single bulb until both sides of the photometer are equally illuminated. Record the distance from the Joly photometer to the light source in cm.

Repeat this procedure with three and finally all four of the bulbs illuminated.

Compare the power of four light bulbs illuminated with the power when one is illuminated.

How does the intensity of light reaching the Joly photometer from the four bulbs compare with the light reaching it when only a single bulb is connected?

How do the intensities on both sides of the Joly photometer compare when they appear equally bright?

Intensity (No. of bulbs)	Distance (single bulb to photometer)			
1				
2				
3				
4				

3. Complete the chart. Plot a graph of intensity versus distance. What kind of result do you get?

Suggest how the data might be plotted to obtain a straight-line graph.

4. Rearrange the data in such a manner as you think will produce a straight-line graph when plotted. Use the available space in the table for this data.

How does the intensity vary with the distance from the point source?

Write the equation relating intensity and distance. What property of the light bulb does the constant represent?

Does background illumination on the screen, such as the reflection from a white shirt, cause errors in your results? Discuss.

5. A light bulb illuminates a screen from a distance of 4 m. This bulb is replaced by a second bulb having 4 times the power. Where must the second bulb be placed in order to produce the same intensity on the screen as the first bulb?

Waves Propagated in One Dimension

Energy can be transferred from one position in space to another by the transfer of particles. Waves carry energy from one point to another without transferring matter. This experiment marks the beginning of a detailed study of wave motion. You should constantly compare the properties of waves and light as you perform these experiments.

Introduction

To study the propagation of wave pulses in a linear medium.

Purpose

Apparatus

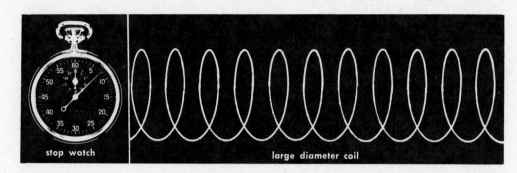

stop watch   large diameter coil

1. Stretch a large diameter coil along the floor to a total length of about 8 m. Create a pulse in the coil by snapping your arm out a small distance at right angles to the length of the coil and back to its initial position without over-shooting this position. Describe the shape of the pulse. Does the shape change as the pulse travels along? Does its amplitude change?

Method

Create a fairly large pulse. With a stop watch, measure the time the pulse takes to travel one length of the coil and record. Create an identical pulse. Measure the time it takes the pulse to travel back and forth once on the coil. How do these times compare? Does the speed of the pulse change with position along the coil? How could you test your prediction?

Create pulses of various shapes and sizes. Does size or shape affect the speed of propagation of the pulse? If the shape of a pulse stays the same, what must be true about the speed?

63

2. Decrease the stretch of the coil. What effect does this have on the tension? Create a large pulse. Measure the length of time it takes to go the length of the coil and return. How does tension affect the speed of the pulse?

What effect would an increase in tension have on pulse speed?

3. Arrange to send pulses toward one another from opposite ends of the coil. They must be sent down the same side at the same time, and have the same amplitude. What happens to the amplitude of the medium where they coincide? Did one pulse have any lasting effect on the other? Do crossed light beams interact? Discuss.

When the pulses meet, how does the maximum amplitude of the resultant pulse compare with the amplitude of each of its component pulses?

Repeat this for pulses of different amplitudes on the same side of the coil. What do you conclude?

4. Send pulses down opposite sides of the coil from opposite ends having the same amplitude. What is the amplitude of the medium where they coincide?

Send two pulses of different amplitude down opposite sides of the coil. What conclusion do you draw?

By referring to your text, state the Principle of Superposition.

5. Two waves, having amplitudes as drawn, coincide as shown in the diagram. Determine the nature of the resultant wave by applying the Principle of Superposition.

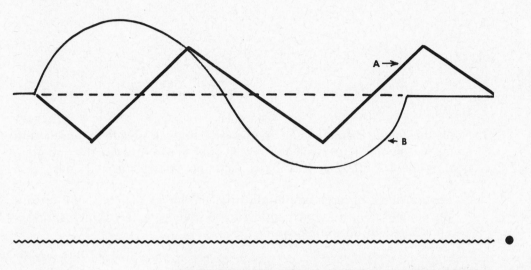

―――――――――――――――――――――――――――――――― •

LINEAR PULSES, TRANSMISSION AND REFLECTION Expt. #22

Waves often travel from one medium to another. Can waves be reflected and transmitted at the same time at a junction? Waves must do this if they are to explain the behavior of light.

Introduction

To study the transmissive and reflective properties of waves.

Purpose

Apparatus

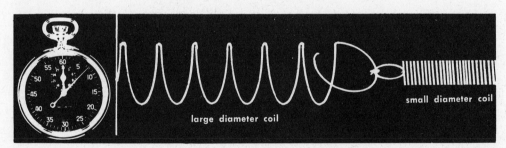

large diameter coil

small diameter coil

1. Hold one end of the large diameter coil rigid. Stretch the coil to a length of about 8 m. Send a large horizontal pulse toward the rigid end. On which side of the coil is the reflected pulse in relation to the incident pulse? What happens to the phase of a wave on reflecting from the rigid end? Sketch the reflected pulse.

Method

2. Attach a 2m length of thread or light string to one end of the large coil. Stretch the coil to a length of about 8 m by pulling the end of the thread. The end of the coil attached to the thread is considered to be a free end. Send a large pulse toward this free end. What happens to the phase of a wave on reflecting at the free end? Sketch the reflected pulse. Compare the speed of the pulse on the thread with that on the coil.

3. Hook the larger diameter coil to the smaller coil. Secure it firmly with string. Grasp the large coil about 2/3 of the way toward the junction, holding the 2/3 firmly in your hand. Carefully stretch the two coils.

   (a) Send a pulse of large amplitude from the larger diameter coil toward the smaller coil. In which spring is the speed greater? Which spring is considered to be the heavier?

   What happens at the junction? How does the reflected pulse compare in attitude to the incident pulse? Sketch the results.

   (b) Send a pulse of large amplitude from the smaller coil toward the larger. What happens at the junction? Compare the attitude of the reflected pulse with the incident pulse. Compare the attitudes of the transmitted and incident pulses. Sketch the results.

4. (a) When the incident pulse travels from a heavier toward a lighter medium, how does the reflected pulse compare in attitude to the incident pulse?

(b) When the incident pulse travels from a lighter toward a heavier medium, compare the attitude of the reflected pulse with that of the incident pulse.

5. A pulse of amplitude 1 cm travels toward the junction. The speed of pulses in medium A is 3 cm/sec and in medium B is 1.5 cm/sec. The center of the pulse at the instant shown is 6 cm from the junction. After 3 sec, show the nature and position of the pulses in each medium.

6. A triangular pulse of amplitude 2 cm and length 2 cm is created in the center of medium A, of length 8 cm. The speed of pulses in media A, B and C are 2 cm/sec, 1 cm/sec, and 4 cm/sec, respectively. On the diagram provided, sketch the nature of the pulses in each medium after 1 sec and 3 secs.

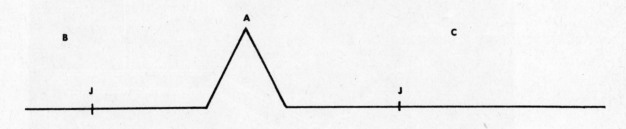

after 1 sec

after 3 sec

Waves Propagated in Two Dimensions

Expt. #23   **PULSES IN A TWO-DIMENSIONAL MEDIUM**

Introduction   The ripple tank is more useful than the coil for studying the behavior of waves since the wave motion can take place in all directions on the surface of the water. This experiment will familiarize you with the operation of a ripple tank. It is a simple matter to generate waves in a still pond. Circular wave fronts can be created by dropping a small object, such as a pebble, into the water or by bobbing a small circular object up and down. To produce plane waves, a straight-edged object having some length is necessary. The still pond in this experiment is the ripple tank.

Purpose   To study the production, propagation and reflection of circular and plane wave fronts from straight and curved barriers.

Apparatus

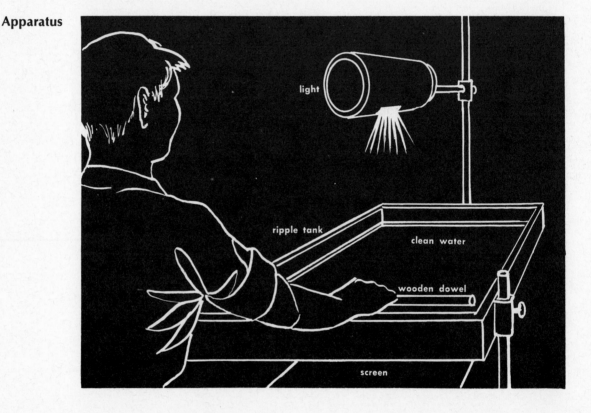

Method   Add clean water to the ripple tank until a uniform depth of about 0.75 cm is achieved as determined by measuring the depth at each corner.

1. Touch the center of the ripple tank with your finger. What do you observe in the tank? Explain the formation of the bright region and the dark region

on the screen with the aid of a diagram and by using the properties of lenses.

What evidence do you have that the speed of the pulse on the surface of the water is the same in all directions?

2. Position the long rod (dowel) horizontally in the water parallel to, and a few cm from, one side. Roll the dowel forward a small fraction of a revolution by placing your hand palm downward on the dowel and pushing forward about 1 cm. Practice until you are able to create a straight, distinct pulse as viewed on the screen. Is there any change in the shape of the pulse as it moves down the tank? If so, explain.

What takes place near the outer edges? Why?

In what direction are the pulses moving relative to the axis of the wave front? What name did we give to a vector representing the direction of travel of light? What name might you give to the direction of travel of the wave front?

3. Place a straight reflecting barrier in the ripple tank. Place the dowel parallel to the barrier and generate pulses. What angle does the direction of travel make with the wave front? With the reflecting barrier? What is the angle of incidence? How do they reflect? How does this result compare with the reflection of a parallel beam of light shone at a plane mirror?

4. Place the dowel at various angles to the barrier creating straight pulses at different angles of incidence. Are the reflected pulses straight? Compare the angle of reflection with the angle of incidence in each case.

5. To determine if the angle of incidence is always equal to the angle of reflection, we must test various-shaped pulses incident on various-shaped reflecting barriers. Touch the water close to the plane reflecting barrier with your finger. Describe the shape of the pulse before reflection and after reflection.

Where does the reflected pulse appear to originate? What name did we give to this type of source when studying light? Compare the reflection of circular waves from a straight barrier with the reflection of light from a point source using a plane mirror.

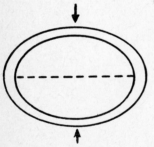

cross-section of rubber tubing

6. Place the circular reflecting barrier in the water. Touch the water in the middle of the circle. What do you observe? Neglecting friction, describe the motion of the pulse over a period of time.

Give the barrier an elliptical shape by squeezing the circular barrier as shown above. Touch the water with your finger at various positions along the long axis of the ellipse. What do you notice as you touch it about a quarter of the way along the long axis?

Touch the water at other positions. How many foci does an ellipse have? How would light from a point source behave if the light source was placed at these positions within an elliptical light reflector?

7. Remove the curved barrier. Create a large right-angled barrier halfway down the ripple tank as shown. Shield the left portion of the right angle from the incident plane wave by placing a barrier halfway across the tank. Create a plane wave pulse. Describe in detail how the plane wave front reflects from the two sides of the right angle.

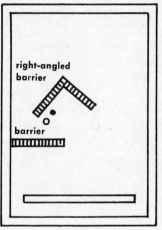

plane wave generator

Turn the right-angled barrier slightly, each time creating a plane wave front. Describe how the plane wave front reflects.

Touch the water with your finger at O. What is the shape of the pulse after having reflected from both edges of the right-angled barrier? Compare this result with the result obtained using a point light source and two plane mirrors at right angles.

8. Bend a length of rubber tubing setting it up in the shape of a parabola as shown below.

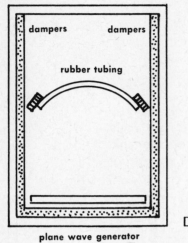

Diagram A

plane wave generator

Use this as the reflecting barrier and reflect straight pulses. What do you observe when you use the tubing to reflect the straight pulses? Sketch on Diagram A the position of a pulse at equal time intervals until it disappears. What do the pulses seem to do after reflection?

Locate and mark the position on the screen where the straight pulses seem to converge after reflection. Create another straight pulse and follow the motion of several of the small segments that make it up. Indicate the direction of motion of each segment on the diagram above. How did you represent this direction? Where did the lines drawn to indicate this motion converge?

To what does this correspond in the geometrical study of light?

Create a circular pulse at the parabola's focus. Note the shape of this pulse after reflection. Can you obtain the same effect by creating the circular pulse at a location other than the focal point?

9. Summarize the evidence this experiment has provided to indicate that the angle of incidence is equal to the angle of reflection.

~~~~~~ ●

PERIODIC WAVES IN A TWO-DIMENSIONAL MEDIUM Expt. #24

Introduction

The *universal wave equation* $V = f\lambda$, where V represents velocity, f represents frequency, and λ represents wavelength, is true for all periodic travelling waves. A *periodic wave* is a regularly recurring disturbance which travels through a medium without taking the medium along with it. The *period* of a wave is the time taken for one complete wavelength to pass a given point while the *frequency* is the number of complete wavelengths that pass a given point in a given time. In the following experiment we apply the universal wave relationship to waves in a ripple tank.

Earlier in the course you studied how to use a stroboscope to determine object frequencies. When the motion of a vibrating object is "stopped" with one slit of the stroboscope open, how does the frequency of a vibrating object compare with the frequency of the stroboscope? Discuss.

How do you check to see that the true frequency of the vibrating object is not a multiple of the look frequency of the stroboscope? Discuss.

In the following experiment you will be using the stroboscope with either 2 or 4 equally spaced slits open, at your discretion. When the waves are correctly "stopped" with 2 slits open, how does the frequency of the wave compare with the frequency of the stroboscope? Discuss.

With 4 slits open, how does it compare? Discuss.

Purpose To produce and measure the characteristics of straight periodic waves in a ripple tank.

Apparatus

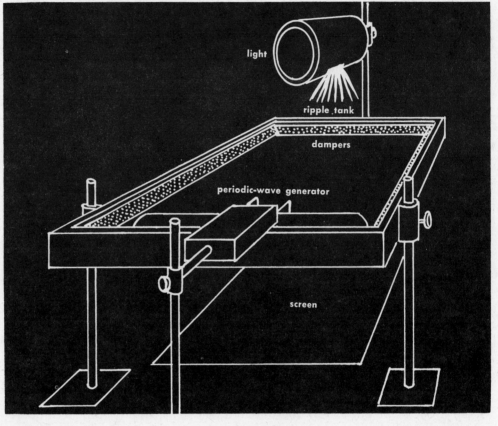

Method Set up the wave generator, ripple tank, and light source as shown. Adjust the water depth to between 0.5 and 0.75 cm and position the dampers as shown. Change the frequency of the wave generator until a fairly low steady frequency is obtained without stalling the motor. Using a stroboscope with either two or four slits open, "stop" the wave motion as seen on the paper screen. Make sure you have the correct "stopping" frequency.

1. (a) Create low frequency periodic waves and when you have their motion correctly "stopped" using the stroboscope, begin counting quietly out loud.

   (b) Using a wave generator at the same frequency as before, use the stroboscope to "stop" the wave pattern. Have your partner determine the average wavelength of the waves on the screen by placing two markers, such as pencils, parallel to and on two "stopped" wave fronts 5 wavelengths apart. Measure the distance between the pencils. Record in the table and calculate the wavelength.

	Time for 20 vibrations of stroboscope (sec)	Number of vibrations per second	Number of slits open	Frequency of wave	Distance across 5 wavelengths (cm)	Image wavelength	True wavelength
1							
2							
3							
4							

You have now measured the wavelength of the image on the screen. By calculation, find the true wavelength and record in the chart. Show the complete calculation including a diagram for one of the values in the space provided.

(c) Repeat (a) and (b) several times with the wave generator at slightly *different* frequencies but *still slow*. Record the values as before, and calculate the frequency and wavelength of the wave.

(d) Using the values for frequency and wavelength, calculate the velocity of the disturbance in each case.

Calculations of Velocity

	Frequency (sec $^{-1}$)	Wavelength (cm)	Velocity (cm/sec)
1			
2			
3			
4			

(e) Determine the average velocity of the water waves. Is there much deviation of individual velocities from this average?

2. In order to perform a cross-check on the average velocity obtained using the universal wave equation, replace the periodic wave generator with the wooden dowel. Create a straight pulse at one end of the ripple tank and, using a stop watch, time its travel to the opposite end by observing the image on the screen. Repeat this a number of times to determine an average time of travel. Measure the distance travelled by the pulse in the tank. Calculate the average velocity.

True distance (cm)	Average time (sec)	Average velocity (cm/sec)

Why was the distance travelled by the image on the screen not used in determining the velocity of the water waves?

How do the two values for average velocity compare? Which do you think is the more accurate? Discuss.

3. Place a barrier in the ripple tank as shown below. Create straight periodic waves. What happens to the waves at this barrier?

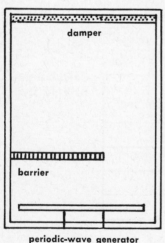

damper

barrier

periodic-wave generator

How many wave trains are travelling in the water between the barrier and generator at any one instant?

Compare their speeds.

Compare their directions of motion.

The superimposed patterns of the incident and reflected waves interfere to form a "stopped" pattern. Measure the distance between two adjacent flashing bright bars in this pattern and compare it with the distance between two adjacent bright bars in a travelling wave.

Explain why the bright bars appear to flash on and off.

Measure the distance across 10 bright bars and calculate the wavelength for the standing wave pattern.

The stroboscope was not necessary to "stop" the repetitive motion in this case. Why?

4. Add water to the ripple tank to a depth of about 1.5 cm. Remove the reflecting barriers and create low frequency periodic waves. Maintaining the generator at this frequency, slowly siphon water from the ripple tank. What happens to the wavelength as the depth decreases?

From the universal wave equation, by maintaining f constant and increasing λ, what happens to the value for V?

What happens to the velocity of a disturbance as the water is made shallower?

5. Recall that light refracts and changes speed if it enters a different medium at an oblique angle. Describe how the results obtained in Part 4 could be used to devise an experiment to test the refraction of water waves?

6. You are observing a pattern of periodic plane waves from a ripple tank on a screen located 60 cm below the surface of the water, through a hand stroboscope having 3 open slits. When the pattern is correctly "stopped" on the screen, your partner places a pencil on the third and another on seventh bright bar. The stroboscope makes 20 revolutions in 15 seconds. The distance from the filament of the bulb to the water is 45 cm and the distance between the pencils is 15 cm.

(a) Determine the speed of the waves in the ripple tank.

(b) If you adjust the frequency of the wave generator to 6 vib/sec, 8 vib/sec, 10 vib/sec, and 16 vib/sec, determine the wavelength of the water waves corresponding to each frequency.

(c) Plot a graph of wavelength versus frequency using the values calculated above. Describe the relationship between frequency and wavelength, using additional graphs if necessary.

Expt. #25 **WATER WAVES IN A TWO-DEPTH MEDIUM**

Introduction The speed of water waves can be changed by varying the depth of the water. Two different depths of water may be analogous to two different media, and the boundary between the two can be considered the interface between the two media. Do water waves change direction and speed in a way similar to light, and do they obey Snell's Law?

We will refer to the angle between the incident wave front and boundary as the angle of incidence and the angle between the refracted wave front and boundary as the angle of refraction since they are equivalent to these angles.

Purpose To study the refraction of waves in a ripple tank.

Apparatus As in Experiment 24.

Method 1. Place a glass plate on supports in about 1.5 cm of water, with its longer straight edge parallel to the straight wave generator and its top surface about 0.1 cm below the water. Start the wave generator and adjust it to a low frequency of less than 10 vib/sec. How does the direction each wave front is travelling compare with the direction of the boundary between deep and shallow water?

What visible changes in wavelength and speed do you notice as the waves travel from deep to shallow water?

2. Observe the wave pattern through a rotating hand stroboscope. Can you "stop" the motion in both regions of the ripple tank by rotating the stroboscope at one frequency? Compare the frequency of the wave fronts in deep and shallow water.

3. Turn the glass plate until the near edge makes an angle of approximately 30° with the plane wave generator. Produce periodic waves of constant low frequency, maintaining the frequency throughout this part of the experiment. "Stop" the pattern as viewed through the stroboscope. Mark the direction of the deep-shallow boundary, the incident wave front and the refracted wave front on the screen. Measure the angle of incidence ($\angle i$) and the angle of refraction ($\angle R$) and record. Repeat this procedure for angles of incidence of 45° and 60° recording $\angle i$ and $\angle R$ each time. Are the refracted waves straight? In what direction does the wave front bend in going from deep to shallow water? (Discuss this by comparing $\angle i$ with $\angle R$).

Trial	$\angle i$	$\angle R$	sin $\angle i$	sin $\angle R$	sin $\angle i$ / sin $\angle R$
1					
2					
3					

Using tables, determine the values of sin $\angle i$, sin $\angle R$ and the refractive index sin $\angle i$ / sin $\angle R$. How constant are the values? Why would you expect a large variation?

Determine the average refractive index showing your calculations.

4. Use the generator with the same frequency as in Part 3. Position the glass plate until its near edge makes an angle of about 30° with the generator. "Stop" the pattern as viewed through the stroboscope. Mark the position of 2 adjacent refracted crests and 2 adjacent incident crests. Measure the magnified wavelength in both the shallow area and the deep area by measuring the distance between the adjacent crests. Record.

λ shallow (cm)	λ deep (cm)

Assuming that the frequency is the same in the two depths of water, show that the ratio of the magnified wavelengths (λ deep/λ shallow) is equal to the ratio of the velocities (V deep/V shallow).

Determine the ratio, V deep/V shallow, showing your calculations.

How does this compare to the average refractive index determined in Part 3?

5. Use the apparatus as set up in Part 1, but give the generator a frequency as slow as possible without stalling the motor. Observe the wave pattern through a rotating hand stroboscope and "stop" the motion on the screen. Draw a line or place a pencil parallel to the "stopped" refracted wave front. Increase the frequency of the generator smoothly while viewing the pattern through the stroboscope. What seems to be happening to the direction of the refracted wave front compared to the previous direction indicated by the pencil or line?

Which frequency of waves refract to a greater extent with the same depth of water?

6. It is desirable to make a further test of the results observed in Part 5. Place the elliptical glass plate in the water close to the wave generator with its long axis and the 2 barriers extending out from each end parallel to the wave generator as shown.

Give the generator a low frequency. Describe the shape of the refracted waves on the side of the lens away from the generator. Sketch the pattern.

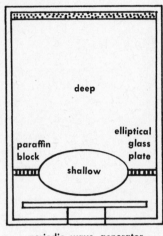

periodic wave generator

What do the refracted wave fronts do farther back in the tank? Of what optical arrangement is this a model?

Very carefully mark the position of the focus on the screen. Increase the frequency of the wave generator. What happens to the wavelength of the incident wave? What happens to the refraction as the frequency is increased? To test this, observe the place where the refracted waves converge as the frequency is increased.

If you had waves of 3 distinct frequencies incident on the glass plate, what would you observe on the screen?

To what property of light does the frequency of a wave seem to correspond?

7. Recall that the speed of light is greater in a vacuum than in glass. Does this wave model agree with the refraction of light better than with the particle model? Elaborate in terms of the speed of the waves and the direction of

bending (direction of travel). Compare the results observed with particles, water waves and light.

8. A plane wave generator of frequency 5 vib/sec creates water waves of wavelength 6.4 cm in region A. The angle between these wave crests and the straight boundary between regions A and B of a ripple tank is 20°. In region B this angle is 33.2°. Calculate:

(a) the relative refractive index of the boundary between the two depth regions

(b) the velocity of the water waves in each region

(c) the wavelength of the water waves in region B

<hr>

Expt. #26   WATER WAVES, SLITS AND OBSTACLES

Introduction   When parallel rays of light from the sun are blocked by an airplane, a shadow of approximately airplane-size is cast on the ground below. A parallel beam of light incident on a keyhole creates an image on a screen on the opposite side almost identical in size and shape. This suggests that light undergoes very little bending around an obstacle and that it tends to cast sharp shadows.

What happens to plane water waves as they encounter an obstacle or an opening? Do wavelength or obstacle size affect the results in any way?

To study the effect of openings and obstacles on the travel of plane water waves in a ripple tank.

As in Experiment 24.

1. Set up a paraffin block barrier parallel to the plane wave generator blocking off half the ripple tank. Place the long side of the bevelled paraffin block next to the generator.

   Create a single sharp plane pulse by rolling the wooden dowel forward through a fraction of a revolution. Show by sketches on Figure A the shape of the pulse in front of the barrier, just past the barrier, and farther back in the tank from the incident wave. Shade the region completely blocked from incident waves on the diagram.

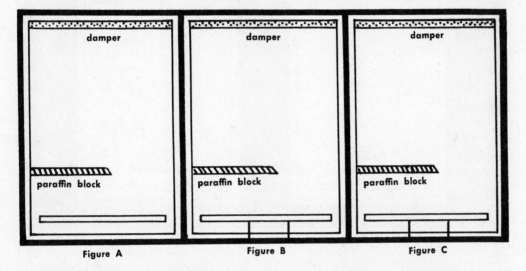

| Figure A | Figure B | Figure C |

   Repeat the procedure, this time comparing the image brightness of the straight and curved portions of the pulse behind the barrier. Which is the more intense? What does this indicate about the amplitude of the curved portion of the wave?

   The curved portion of the wave front is found in that area of the tank which is partially blocked from the incident wave. In order to cause a disturbance in this region, the incident wave must have changed direction. Indicate in Figure A the partially blocked region with crosshatching lines.

2. Create long wavelength (low frequency) periodic waves using the plane wave generator. Note the shadow region and region of diffraction formed on the far side of the barrier. Indicate these regions on Figure B with shaded areas and hatched areas respectively.

   Decrease the wavelength of the periodic waves by about half. Indicate the resulting shadow and partial shadow regions on Figure C. What change

83

takes place in the size of the shadow region as the wavelength decreases?

Under which wavelength condition were the waves diffracted to a greater extent?

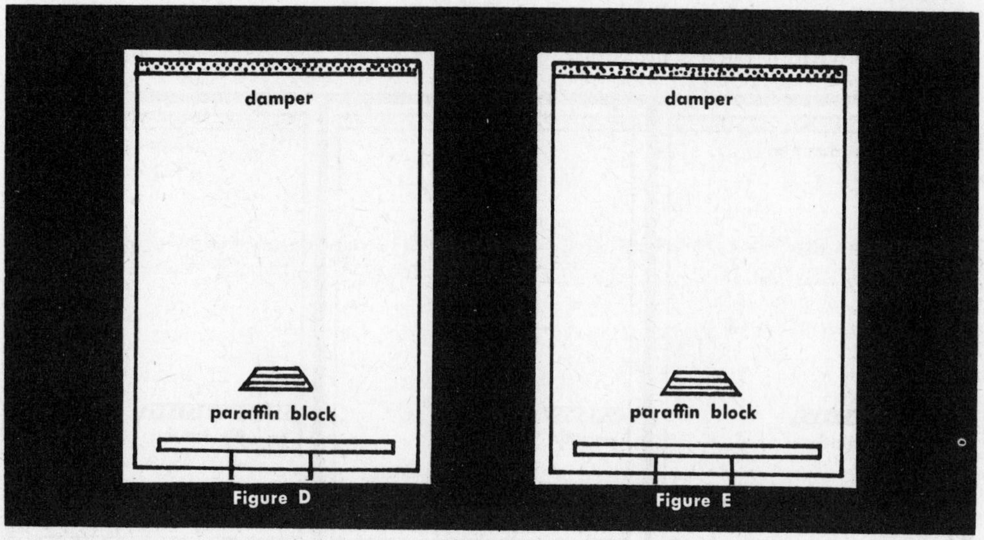

Figure D

Figure E

3. Place a small trapezoidal paraffin block in the ripple tank with its longer side about 10 cm from the plane wave generator. Generate long wavelength periodic waves. Sketch on Figure D the shadow and partial shadow regions. Could you detect the presence of the obstacle by viewing only that portion of the pattern a great distance behind the block? Discuss.

Decrease the wavelength of the periodic waves to half the initial length. Sketch the shadow and partial shadow regions on Figure E. What happens to the size of the partial shadow region as the wavelength is decreased?

Which wavelength creates a more distinct shadow region behind the block? Under which wavelength condition would you expect the obstacle to cast a shadow approximately its own width?

4. Position a pair of bevelled paraffin blocks about 10 cm from the periodic plane wave generator, creating an opening or slit about 3 cm wide. Generate long wavelength plane periodic waves. Sketch the shape of the waves after they have moved through the opening on Figure F. Indicate the shadow and partial shadow regions on the diagram. Do the waves continue to move only in their original direction?

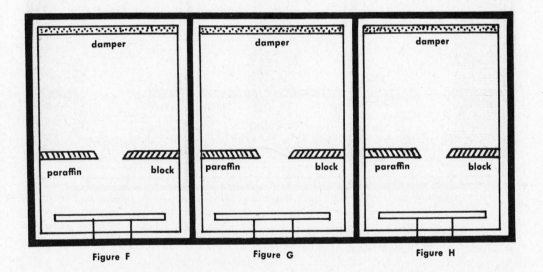

Figure F   Figure G   Figure H

When long wavelength water waves get an appreciable distance beyond the slit, describe the shape of the resulting wave front. To what kind of source is a slit equivalent when using waves of wavelength larger than the slit width?

Decrease the wavelength in two stages, sketching the shape of the waves and indicating the extent of the total and partial shadow regions on Figures G and H.

What happens to the amount of diffraction as the wavelength is decreased while maintaining a constant slit width? Under what wavelength condition would you expect to get a fairly sharp image of the slit? How must the wavelength of waves incident on a slit compare with the slit width if the slit is to act as a point source?

5. Adjust the plane wave generator to produce a medium wavelength periodic wave. Sketch the pattern on Figure I. Decrease the slit width to half. Sketch the pattern on Figure J. Double the slit width from the initial width. Sketch the pattern on Figure K.

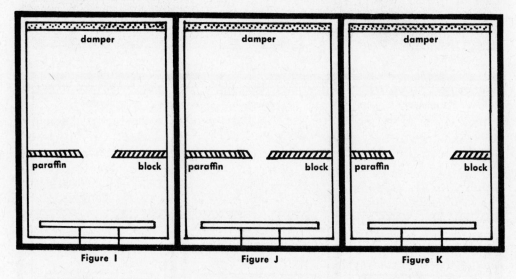

Figure I   Figure J   Figure K

As the slit width is decreased, but the wavelength remains constant, what happens to the amount of diffraction?

6. By referring back to Parts 4 and 5, on what two factors does the amount of diffraction of water waves seem to depend? In what way is it related to each factor?

In a ripple tank experiment using plane periodic water waves of wavelength λ incident on a slit of width w, a specific amount of diffraction was observed. If the student doubles the width of the slit, what change will be necessary in the wavelength in order to produce the initial amount of diffraction? Why?

7. The amount of diffraction when plane periodic water waves encounter the edges of an obstacle or slit is easily visible. Parallel light rays do not produce the same amount of diffraction when incident on these same obstacles. What kind of wavelength might light have?

Interference

INTERFERENCE OF PERIODIC WAVES IN A LINEAR MEDIUM

Expt. #27

Introduction

When two or more waves travel in the same medium at the same time, interference takes place. Whether the interference is constructive or destructive at any given point in the medium depends on the relative phase of the waves where they coincide. If two travelling waves, identical in wavelength and amplitude but travelling in opposite directions, are in the same medium at the same time, a special wave referred to as a "standing wave" is set up. Standing waves can be produced in a ripple tank by reflecting periodic plane water waves from a nearby barrier parallel to the generator. Standing waves can also be produced in a linear medium such as a coil. What is the nature of standing waves?

To produce standing waves in a linear medium and study their properties.

Purpose

Apparatus

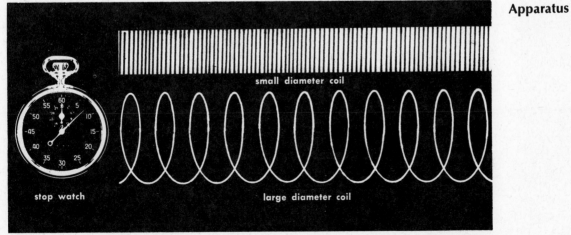

small diameter coil

stop watch

large diameter coil

1. Hold one end of the small diameter coil rigid and give it some tension by stretching it along the floor. Measure the coil length and record it in the table.

Method

(a) Produce a periodic transverse travelling wave by vibrating your hand very slowly back and forth at right angles to the axis of the coil and rolling it in the direction of motion. Vary this frequency until the coil vibrates in one segment or "loop" and continues this motion with little movement of your hand. Determine the time for 20 complete vibrations and record it in the table. Sketch the pattern traced out by the coil.

Begin by vibrating the coil with the same frequency, watching the pulse produced. What fraction of a wavelength do you think is present in the length of one loop? Why?

(b) Without changing the length of the coil, increase the frequency smoothly from that used in (a) until the coil vibrates in two segments or loops. The point of no motion halfway along the coil is called a "node." This is a region of destructive interference. The regions of complete constructive interference in the middle of the vibrating segments are called "antinodes." Why do they refer to the resulting waves as "standing waves?"

Determine the time for 20 complete vibrations and record in the table. How many wavelengths are present in the length of the coil now?

(c) Without changing the coil length increase the frequency smoothly from that used in (b) until you again cause the coil to vibrate in segments. How many loops are now present? How many nodes are present if you include the nodes at each end? How many wavelengths are present in the length of the coil? Determine the time for 20 vibrations and record in the table.

(d) Increase the frequency from that used in (c). Can you produce other patterns of standing waves containing more nodes?

Length of coil = _____ m

Part	Time for 20 vibrations (sec)	Frequency of travelling wave (vib/sec)	Number of wavelengths present in coil length	Wave length (m)	Speed (m/sec)
(a)					
(b)					
(c)					

(e) Determine the speed of the travelling waves by using the frequency and wavelengths determined and by applying the universal wave equation to the readings obtained in (a), (b) and (c). How do the values compare? Determine the average velocity.

2. Stretch the coil to the same length as used in Part 1. Determine the length of time it takes a pulse to travel the length of the coil. From this, determine the speed of the travelling wave. Show your calculations below. How does this answer compare with the average value determined in Part 1? Which method do you think is the more accurate way of determining the speed?

3. Replace the small diameter coil with the large diameter coil. Stretch it to a length identical to that used in Part 1. Produce a standing wave, causing this coil to vibrate in 2 loops. Measure the time for 20 vibrations. Determine the frequency, wavelength and speed of the travelling wave in this medium by completing the chart.

Length of coil = _____ m

Time for 20 vibrations (sec)	Frequency of travelling wave (vib/sec)	Number of wavelengths present in coil length	Wave length (m)	Velocity (m/sec)

Which medium has the greater velocity, the large diameter coil or the small diameter coil? Compare the frequency and wavelength needed to produce similar standing waves in the two coils. Why can standing waves be produced only at certain frequencies in any medium of constant length?

4. Tie a 3 m length of cord to one end of the smaller diameter coil, creating a free end. Give the coil some tension and produce periodic waves by vibrating the coil from the end without the cord attached. Can you set up a standing wave pattern in the coil? If so, in what way is it different from all previous patterns?

5. Hook the large diameter coil to the small diameter coil. Secure it firmly with string. Hold the end of the coil rigid. Grasp the large diameter coil about halfway toward the junction, supporting the loose half in your hand. Can you produce standing waves in the combination? How do the frequencies, the wavelengths and the speeds of the travelling waves compare in the two coils? How must they compare in order to produce standing waves?

~~~~~~

Expt. #28   INTERFERENCE OF WAVES IN A TWO-DIMENSIONAL MEDIUM

Introduction   Standing waves, consisting of nodes (points of destructive interference) and antinodes (points of maximum constructive interference), can be produced in a linear medium by sending identical waves from opposite ends of a coil spring. The pattern produced by two vibrating point sources in a two-dimensional medium, such as on the surface of the water in a ripple tank, should bear some resemblance to that in the linear medium. What are the similarities and differences between these two patterns?

Purpose   To study the interference pattern produced by two inphase periodic point sources.

Apparatus   Ripple tank and accessories, including two inphase point sources.

90 **Method**   1. Place about 1 cm depth of water in a level ripple tank. Attach one point

source to the wave generator. Adjust the wave generator to give periodic waves of about 2 cm wavelength. Describe the pattern observed.

2. Attach a second point source to the generator 6 cm from the first. Adjust the frequency of the generator to give inphase waves of about 2 cm wavelength. How do the frequency, wavelength and direction of motion of the waves compare along the line joining the point sources S_1 and S_2?

Observe the pattern along this line on the screen. Sketch your observations on Figure A.

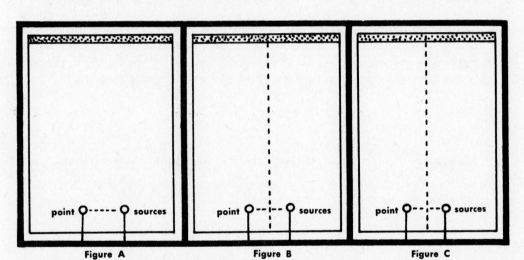

What do the dark regions correspond to in the study of standing waves in a linear medium (the coil spring)?

What kind of interference is taking place at the midpoint between the point sources S_1 and S_2? Why?

3. Generate periodic waves from the two inphase point sources having the same wavelength as before. Study the pattern produced in the ripple tank. Locate the regions where the water is not moving. These are nodal lines or regions of destructive interference. Describe the shape of the nodal lines. What name is given to a curve of this shape?

Compare their shape far from the point sources with their shape closer to the point sources. If they are projected straight back, from where would they appear to originate?

Sketch the number and shape of the nodal lines on Figure B.

4. "Stop" the pattern with a 2-slit or 4-slit stroboscope. Describe the pattern of the constructive interference region between any two adjacent nodal lines.

Is a crest or trough region directly across a nodal line from the end of any crest?

Rotate the stroboscope at a frequency slightly less than that required to stop the waves. In what direction do the waves appear to move compared to their actual direction of motion?

5. Create waves of about 1 cm wavelength by doubling the frequency. Do not change the distance between the point sources S_1 and S_2. How many nodal lines are now present on the screen?

Notice the right bisector of the line joining the point sources S_1 and S_2 in Figure C. Locate this region on the screen. What do you notice about the symmetry of the pattern on either side?

What kind of interference region is situated along this right bisector?

Sketch the number and shape of the nodal lines on Figure C.

Decrease the frequency gradually until 4 cm wavelength waves are produced. What happens to the number of nodal lines as the wavelength increases?

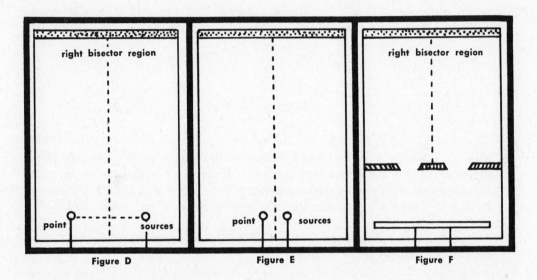

| Figure D | Figure E | Figure F |

6. Adjust the generator to produce waves of about 2 cm wavelength. Double the separation of the point sources to 12 cm. Sketch the number and position of the nodal lines on Figure D.

   Halve the original separation of the point sources to about 3 cm without changing the wavelength. Sketch the number and position of the nodal lines on Figure E.

7. By referring back to your sketches, complete the following chart.

Figure	Approximate source separation d (cm)	Approximate wavelength λ (cm)	Number of nodal lines
B			
C			
D			
E			

(a) What relationship exists between the number of nodal lines and:

(i) source separation?

(ii) wavelength?

(b) Is there any ratio between *d* and λ which will permit you to determine the number of nodal lines?

(c) In order to obtain a significant separation of the nodal lines if small wavelength waves were being studied, what procedures could be used?

8. Remove the two point sources and place the straight wave generator into the water. Place barriers in the positions shown in Figure F to produce 2 slits of equal width separated by about 5 cm. These slits should be about 2 cm wide. Produce periodic plane waves of about 2 cm wavelength.

Are you able to create constructive and destructive regions similar to those obtained with the point sources?

What kind of interference region is located along the right bisector region indicated on Figure F?

What kind of sources could you consider the slits to be?

What effect would decreasing the distance between the slits have on the pattern?

By applying mathematics and the Principle of Superposition to the analysis of   **Introduction**
the interference pattern produced in a ripple tank by two point sources
vibrating in phase, we have derived the following relationships:

Path difference $= PS_1 - PS_2$

$$= (n - \tfrac{1}{2})\lambda$$

$$= \frac{d\,x_n}{L}$$

Where: L = distance from any point P on the nth nodal line to the midpoint
between the point sources,

d = distance between the point sources,

x_n = perpendicular distance from the point P to the center line,

n = number of the nodal line counting from the center line out,

λ = wavelength of the periodic wave, and

S_1 and S_2 are the left and right point sources, respectively.

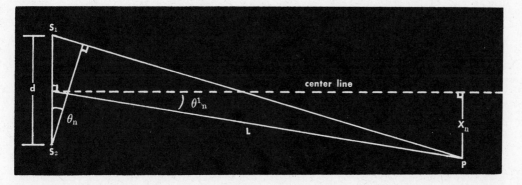

These variables have been indicated on the diagram. We will check this relationship by determining the wavelength of water waves on the screen, using
the interference equations. We will crosscheck this with the wavelength
measured directly from the screen.

To check the following relationships as defined for inphase sources: **Purpose**

$$PS_1 - PS_2 = (n - \tfrac{1}{2})\lambda$$

and

$$\frac{d\,x_n}{L} = (n - \tfrac{1}{2})\lambda$$

As in Experiment 24.   **Apparatus**

1. (a) Attach 2 point sources to the periodic wave generator separated by a   **Method**   95

distance of 5 cm. Adjust the frequency to produce an interference pattern with clearly distinguishable nodal lines. Pick a point P on the third nodal line, far away from the point sources. Measure in cm on the screen the values for PS_1, PS_2, x_n, L, and d. Record all values in the table.

(b) Place a cm ruler along the pattern, perpendicular to any of the moving wave fronts. Stop the pattern, using the 2- or 4-slit stroboscope. Measure the wavelength by superimposing the "stopped" pattern on the ruler and record.

(c) Calculate the wavelength using the equations shown:

(i) $\lambda = \dfrac{PS_1 - PS_2}{(n - 1/2)} =$

n	
PS_1	
PS_2	
x_n	
L	
d	
λ measured	

(ii) $\lambda = \dfrac{d\,x_n}{L\,(n - 1/2)} =$

How does the measured value compare with the calculated values using equation (i)? equation (ii)?

2. Adjust the frequency to give a suitable pattern. Repeat Part 1, but use a source separation of 4 cm and perform the measurement for a point P on the second nodal line, far away from the point sources. Measure the wavelength with the aid of a stroboscope as before. Enter the results in the table and complete the calculations.

(i) $\lambda = \dfrac{PS_1 - PS_2}{(n - 1/2)} =$

n	
PS_1	
PS_2	
x_n	
L	
d	
λ measured	

(ii) $\lambda = \dfrac{d\, x_n}{L\,(n - \frac{1}{2})} =$

How does the measured value compare with the calculated values using equation (i)? equation (ii)?

Under what conditions should equation (ii) give reliable results? Discuss.

What conclusion can you draw regarding these mathematical relationships?

3. Adjust the frequency to produce waves of about 2 cm wavelength using point sources separated by 4 cm. Mark the location of the center line on the screen. What kind of interference region is located along this line?

Adjust the point sources slowly from being in phase to being in opposite phase. When in opposite phase, one point source will touch the water when the other is completely out. What happens to the nodal lines? What kind of an interference region is now along the center line?

If the point sources were rapidly vibrating at random, in and out of phase, would the nodal lines be visible? Discuss.

4. Below is shown part of the interference pattern observed for inphase sources vibrating in a ripple tank. Assume all measurements are to the scale used on the diagram. Apply the equations: (i) $PS_1 - PS_2 = (n - \frac{1}{2})\lambda$

and

(ii) $\dfrac{d\,x_n}{L} = (n - \frac{1}{2})\lambda$

to determine the wavelength, using the points P_2, P_3 and P_4. Obtain the necessary measurements directly from the diagram and enter in the table provided.

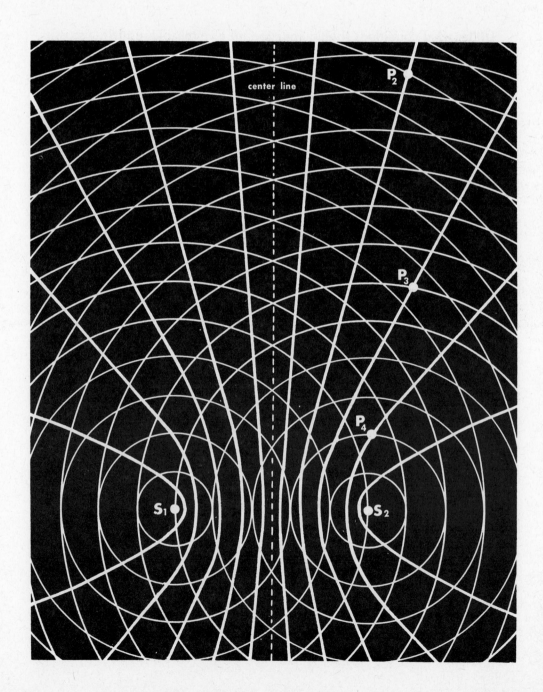

	P_2	P_3	P_4
n			
PS_1			
PS_2			
x_n			
L			
d			
λ measured			
(i) $\lambda = \dfrac{PS_1 - PS_2}{(n - {}^1/_2)} =$			
(ii) $\lambda = \dfrac{d\,x_n}{L\,(n - {}^1/_2)} =$			

(a) Which equation yields more reliable results in every case?

(b) Under what condition(s) are the values calculated using equation (ii) fairly reliable?

~~~~~~ ●

DOUBLE-SLIT INTERFERENCE—YOUNG'S EXPERIMENT

In the experiment on interference in a two-dimensional medium, we observed nodal lines and antinodal lines providing the sources had the same phase or a constant phase delay. From the direction of the nodal lines and the separation of the point sources, we arrived at the equation $\lambda = \dfrac{d\,x_n}{L\,(n - {}^1/_2)}$ for inphase sources. We later simplified this to yield the equation $\lambda = d\,\Delta\,x/L$. Recall that these equations yield reliable results only when the interference pattern is analyzed a large distance from the closely spaced point sources.

From the experiment on diffraction of plane waves around obstacles, we found that as the wavelength decreased the amount of diffraction decreased. From this we suggested that the distinct shadow cast by an object when parallel light rays were incident indicates that light may travel as a short wavelength wave.

With light, if we view 2 light sources in phase or with a constant phase difference, what would be observed at positions corresponding to nodal lines? By measuring the factors in the above equations we should be able to determine the wavelength of light of various colors.

To study the pattern of light produced when it passes through double slits, and determine the wavelength of light of different colors.

Apparatus

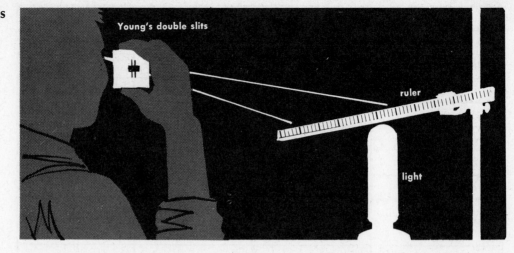

Young's double slits

ruler

light

Method

1. (a) View the luminous filament of a clear showcase bulb through the double slits from a distance of 3 m or more. Describe what you see exactly in the middle of the field of view.

Compare the direction of the bright and dark bands with the direction of the slits. By referring to your text discuss why the fringes near the end of the pattern are colored.

(b) Cover the upper half of the bulb with a blue filter, holding it in place with rubber bands. View the filament through the slits. Describe the differences between the interference pattern for white and blue light.

2. (a) Cover the bulb completely with the blue filter, placing the ruler just behind and slightly above the bulb. View the filament through the slits from a distance of about 3 m and note the number of visible nodal lines superimposed on a given length of the ruler. Record in the table in (d).

(b) Replace the blue filter with the red filter. View red light through the slits. Compare the interference pattern observed for blue light with that observed for red light.

(c) Count the number of visible nodal lines superimposed on the same length of ruler as in (a), viewed from the same distance. Record in the table.

Vary the horizontal angle between the slide containing the slits and the line of sight by turning the slide through an angle of about 45°. What change takes place in the separation of the nodal lines? Explain.

(d)

Color of light viewed	Number of nodal lines counted	Distance interval for the nodal lines
Blue		
Red		

Referring back to interference in the ripple tank, what relationship existed between the wavelength and the number of nodal lines when using point sources (slits) of constant separation?

Use the number of nodal lines counted in the same distance to determine the ratio λ red/λ blue. Show your calculations.

3. (a) View the red light source from a distance of about 100 cm. By super-imposing the nodal lines on the markings of the ruler, determine the distances between a number of visible nodal lines. Note the number of bright fringes enclosed by these nodal lines. This will give you the number of Δx interxals. Record this information in the table.

The double slits on these glass plates were formed by holding two razor blades face to face and forming two parallel scratches on the graphite-covered glass. The separation of the slits was then determined by measuring the thickness of one razor blade with a micrometer screw gauge. Ask your instructor for the distance between the slits if you have not already determined it. Using the recorded information, determine the wavelength of red light in cm and in Angstroms (Å).

Calculations

Total distance between observed dark bands	
Number of bright fringes (#Δx's)	
Average Δx	
Distance between slits d	
Viewing distance from filament L	

(b) Repeat the procedure for the blue light. Record all information in the table.

Calculations

Total distance between observed dark bands	
Number of bright fringes (#Δx's)	
Average Δx	
Distance between slits d	
Viewing distance from filament L	

(c) Using the wavelengths calculated in (a) and (b), determine the ratio λ red/λ blue. Compare this ratio with that obtained in Part 2 (d).

4. Set up the double slits at an accurately measured distance from the sodium yellow source slit. By using the same procedure as in Part 3, complete the table and calculate the wavelength of sodium yellow light in Å.

Calculations

Total distance between observed dark bands	
Number of bright fringes (#Δx's)	
Average Δx	
Distance between slits d	
Viewing distance from filament L	

The correct value for the wavelength of sodium yellow is 5893 Å. Calculate the percentage error of your measurement showing the calculations below.

Expt. #31   SINGLE-SLIT INTERFERENCE EFFECTS

Introduction In Experiment 26 (Water Waves, Slits and Obstacles), we found that a slit acted as a point source of waves only when its width was less than the wavelength incident on it. You probably noticed in the same experiment that, as the slit width was made larger than the wavelength, what we now refer to as nodal lines were observed. It should be possible to obtain a similar effect by observing the showcase lamp through a single slit which is wider than the wavelength of the light used.

Purpose To study the interference pattern produced by a single slit and to compare it to the 2-slit interference pattern.

Apparatus As in Experiment 30.

Method 1. View the luminous filament of a clear showcase bulb from a distance of 3 m or more through the double slits used in the last experiment. Carefully slide an opaque sharp straight-edged cover, such as a razor blade, along the slide until it closes one of the double slits. By sliding this cover back and forth, compare the interference pattern observed through a single slit with that observed through the double slits. Compare the width of the central bright region with those adjacent to it. These bright regions are called maxima.

Compare the intensities of the central and side maxima.

Compare the colored fringes at the edges of the interference pattern.

2. (a) Cover the bulb with the blue filter holding it in place with rubber bands. View the filament through the single and double slits. State the similarities and differences between the two patterns.

(b) Interchange the blue and red filters. Again view the filament through the single and double slits. Compare the central and side maxima.

3. (a) View the red light through several single slits of different widths. These can be made by scratching straight lines on the graphite-coated slide using sharp objects of different widths. Describe the change in the pattern as the width of the viewing slit is increased while the wavelength and the distance from source remain constant.

What happens to the width of the central maximum as the slit width increases?

What relationship might exist between slit width (w) and the perpendicular distance from a point (P) on the first nodal line to the center line (x)? Write a possible proportionality statement.

(b) View the red light through one of the narrower slits. Move twice as close and then twice as far away from the bulb noting the change in the width of the central maximum while the slit width and wavelength remain constant.

What relationship might exist between the perpendicular distance to the first nodal line (x) and the viewing distance (L)? Write a possible proportionality statement.

(c) Cover the lower half of the bulb with the red filter and the upper half with the blue filter. View red and blue light through the same single slit, at the same distance from the bulb. Keep the slit width (w) and viewing distance (L) constant. Which color produces the wider central maximum? Which color has the larger wavelength?

What relationship might exist between the perpendicular distance to the first nodal line (x) and the wavelength (λ)?

(d) By referring back to the results of (a), (b) and (c), write a possible proportionality statement between the perpendicular distance to the first nodal line and the wavelength, slit width and viewing distance.

4. Cover up one of the double slits used in the double-slit interference experiment and view the red light through the single slit. Given that the wavelength of the red light is 6100 Å, determine the width of one of the slits making up the double slits. The equation for any nodal line of the single slit interference pattern is $\sin \theta_n = x/L = n \lambda/w$, where n is the number of the nodal line chosen.

How does this slit width compare to the wavelength of light used?

Should a single-slit interference pattern affect the double-slit interference pattern of the previous experiment? Discuss.

~~~~~~

Expt. #32   **INTERFERENCE EFFECTS WITH THIN FILMS**

Introduction   You have probably noticed the many-colored regions present when light reflects from a film of oil on the surface of water. This is caused by the interference of the light reflected from the film.

To study the interference pattern produced when light is reflected from a thin soap film. **Purpose**

Wire loop, soap-glycerine solution, showcase light source. **Apparatus**

Method

1. Dip the wire loop (of a test tube brush, or similar instrument) vertically into a soap solution to which a little glycerine has been added. Permit light from the clear showcase bulb to reflect from the soap film. View the film from the same side as the light is incident. Describe the bands seen in the film.

   Are the bands straight and stationary? Why?

   What is the color of the band at the top of the loop?

   Where do you think the soap film is the thinnest? Why?

2. Cover the clear bulb with the blue filter and again view the film by reflection. What are the similarities and differences between the white light and the blue light patterns?

   What is the color of the band where the film is thinnest? Explain.

3. Cover the clear bulb with the red filter. What are the similarities and differences between the blue light and the red light patterns? Which light has the longer wavelength? What evidence do you have that this is so?

4. Why are the horizontal bands more widely spaced at the top than at the bottom?

How much does the thickness of the film increase from the center of one dark band to the center of the next dark band in terms of wavelengths? Indicate your reasoning.

Assume the wavelength of the red light to be 6100 Å. How much has the film increased in thickness going from one dark band to the next, expressed in Å?

Under what conditions will the light reflected be:

(i) a maximum?

(ii) a minimum?

━━

Expt. #33   INTERFERENCE OF LIGHT USING AIR WEDGES

Introduction   Air in the shape of a thin wedge can also result in the interference of light waves. This will provide us with a cross-check for the wavelength of sodium yellow light determined in the earlier double-slit experiment.

Purpose   1. To determine the wavelength of sodium yellow light.

2. To determine the thickness of a thin material, such as aluminum foil, using the interference of light of a known wavelength.

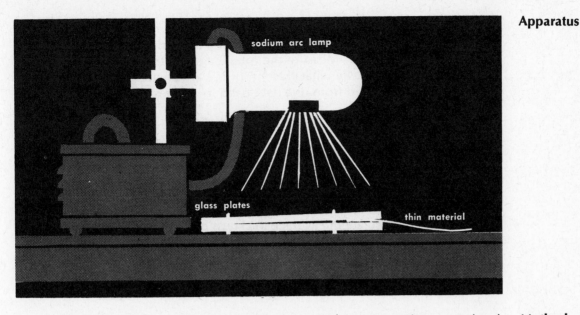

1. Lay 2 long, clean, planed glass plates on top of one another on a level surface. Illuminate them perpendicularly, using the light from a sodium arc lamp. What do you see?

   Are the glass plates perfectly clear and flat? Discuss.

2. To create a thin air wedge, separate the glass plates at one end and insert a single thin cigarette paper between them. Lay a transparent millimeter (mm) ruler along the glass plates. Wrap rubber bands around the glass plates to keep the complete assembly in place. Illuminate the plates perpendicularly with sodium yellow light and view the plates by reflection at an angle of close to 90° to the direction of the near plate.

   What do you observe?

   Explain if the observed lines are not straight or equally spaced.

3. Count the number of bright fringes over a measured distance. (Consider one bright fringe to be from the center of a dark fringe to the center of an adjacent dark fringe.) Measure the total length of the air wedge. Enter the results in the table. By what fraction of a wavelength has the thickness of the air film increased from one dark band to the next?

4. By measuring the thickness of a known number of cigarette papers with a micrometer, calculate the average thickness of one in cm. What assumption have you made?

5. Repeat all measurements several times. Enter all results in the table provided. Average the results and from this determine the average wavelength of sodium yellow light.

	Trial 1	Trial 2	Trial 3	Average
Number of bright fringes				////////
Distance across bright fringes				////////
Average distance between dark bands				
Total length of air wedge				
Maximum thickness of air wedge				

Calculations

110

6. (a) The accepted value for the wavelength of sodium yellow light is 5893 Å. Calculate the percentage difference of your measurement.

   (b) How does the value obtained using the air wedge compare with the value obtained using Young's double slits?

7. (a) Separate the plates, replace the cigarette paper with one thickness of aluminum foil, and secure the setup as before. Repeat the experiment to determine the thickness of the inserted material. Assume the wavelength of sodium yellow light is 5893 Å.

   (b) Cross-check your answer using a micrometer screw gauge and indicate the percentage difference.

   (c) What limits the range of thicknesses of material that can be measured with this air wedge?

8. In measuring the wavelength of light from a cadmium lamp, the following data were obtained: thickness of paper = 0.0013 cm, length of air wedge = 7.7 cm, width of 10 interference bands = 1.9 cm. Calculate:

   (i) the wavelength of this light

(ii) the frequency of this light

~~~~~~

Expt. #34   LIGHT WAVES—TRANSVERSE OR LONGITUDINAL?

Introduction   From previous experiments you have seen that light waves can undergo reflection, refraction, diffraction and interference—properties common to both longitudinal and transverse waves. In a longitudinal wave each particle vibrates back and forth parallel to the direction of travel of the wave. There is only one possible vibration direction, depending on the direction of wave travel. A transverse wave, however, can vibrate in an infinite number of directions perpendicular to its direction of travel. If, on passing such a wave through a special filter, we can remove some directions of vibration of the wave, we would expect a decrease in intensity. The wave would then have properties in one direction perpendicular to the direction of travel that would be different from those in another. It would be said to be "plane polarized." Only transverse waves can be plane polarized. Is a light wave transverse or longitudinal?

Purpose   To use a mechanical model to illustrate the meaning of plane polarization of waves, and to determine if light can be plane polarized.

Apparatus

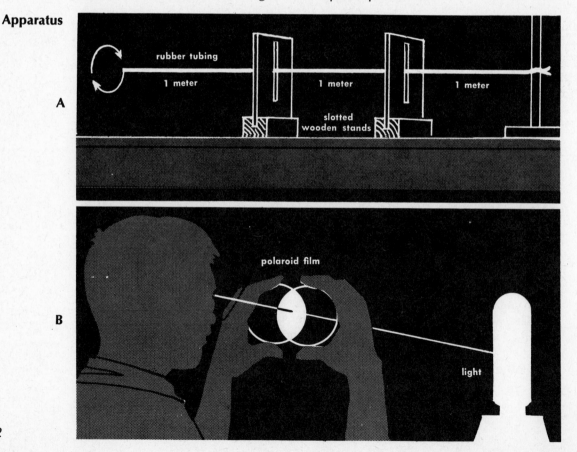

112

1. (a) Assemble 2 wooden stands with upright slots. Place the stands about 1 m apart. Attach a 3 m length of rubber tubing to a rigid support and pass it through the wooden slots. Stretch it about 0.25 m, passing it through the middle of the slots.

   (b) Move your hand in a circular motion to produce transverse waves in all planes at right angles to the axis of the rubber tubing. In what direction are the transverse waves vibrating after passing through the first slot?

   In what direction are the waves plane polarized?

   Does the second slot have any effect on the waves? Discuss.

2. Arrange the second slot at right angles to the first. Again produce transverse waves in all planes at right angles to the axis of the rubber tubing. Describe the motion of the rubber tubing after passing through the second slot.

   What would happen if the slot widths were both made larger?

   How much energy would be transmitted to the other end of the rubber tubing if the slot widths were made equal in size to the diameter of the rubber tubing and all materials were frictionless?

3. View a clear showcase bulb through a single piece of polaroid film. Compare the intensity of the light reaching your eye with and without the polaroid present.

Rotate the polaroid through 360°. Is there any change in the intensity of the light transmitted to your eye?

4. Place a second polaroid between your eye and the first polaroid. Rotate one of the polaroids. What do you notice?

Through what angle must the polaroid be rotated in order to change the transmitted light from maximum to minimum intensity?

Can light be polarized? Discuss.

Does light have the properties of a transverse or a longitudinal wave? Why?

5. View the light reflected from a non-metallic surface such as the desk top through a single polaroid. Rotate the polaroid. What do you observe? Change the viewing angle and repeat the procedure. By referring to books in the library, give an explanation for your observations.

Unit III

MECHANICS

~~~~~~

Law of Inertia and Newton's Law

Motion in the Earth's Gravitational Field

Momentum and Conservation of Momentum

Work and Kinetic Energy

Potential Energy

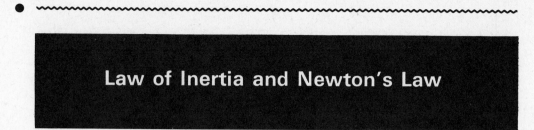

Law of Inertia and Newton's Law

Expt. #35   **THE EFFECT ON VELOCITY OF A CONSTANT UNBALANCED FORCE**

Introduction   Up to this time we have been studying motion, a branch of mechanics called "kinematics." It is equally important, however, to understand the factors causing motion. This branch of mechanics is called "dynamics." When the word dynamics is used, we immediately think of an explosion or a force. You know from everyday experience that a force must be applied to start an object moving from rest or to change its velocity while moving. But how does the magnitude of the force affect this motion? This will be investigated.

Purpose   To study the effect of a constant unbalanced force applied to a body.

Apparatus

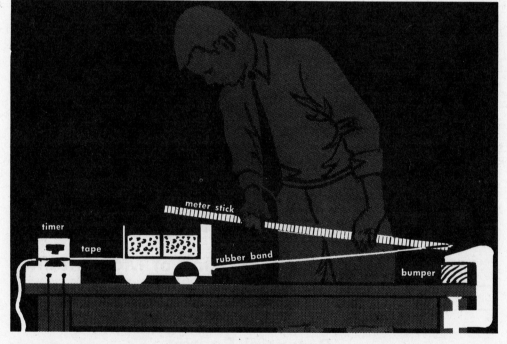

Method   1. If the lab table does not provide a long enough runway for this experiment, clamp a plywood sheet to the table. Clamp the wooden bumper to one end of the runway and the electric timer to the other. Place a cart loaded with 2 bricks on the runway.

2. In order to exert a constant unbalanced force on the cart, attach one end of a single rubber band to the end of the cart away from the timer. Hook the opposite end of the loop over the zero end of a meter stick. Have your partner hold the cart at rest while you stretch the rubber loop sufficiently

to cause the cart, when released, to gather speed slowly as it moves across the table. To ensure a constant stretch, maintain the number on the meter stick adjacent to the cart in a fixed position relative to the cart by moving along with the speeding cart. Practice this procedure until you are able to maintain a constant stretch.

3. Attach a paper tape to the "2-brick" cart. Maintain a constant force as practiced and run off a tape, labelling this tape "2-brick."

4. Repeat the above procedure with a new tape, but place 4 bricks on the cart. Stretch the same rubber band to the same extent as before. Label this tape "4-brick."

5. Mark off the "2-brick" and "4-brick" tapes into 10-tick intervals, called tocks, estimating the initial tock as carefully as possible. Measure the displacement (in cm) travelled in each tock, recording the data in the table provided. Calculate the average velocity during each tock interval. Plot a velocity-time graph for each tape on the same graph paper. Remember that when plotting an average velocity as an instantaneous velocity, it must be plotted at half time in the tock interval. For example, the average velocity calculated for the first tock should be plotted at 0.5 tock.

2-brick tape			4-brick tape		
Time (tock)	Displacement (cm)	Average velocity (cm/tock)	Time (tock)	Displacement (cm)	Average velocity (cm/tock)

6. Describe the slope of the lines in the graph. What relationship exists between the change in velocity and the time interval? Compare the change in velocity during the first 4 tocks with the change during the next 4 tocks.

By referring to the graph, indicate the effect an increase in the mass, to which the constant unbalanced force is applied, has on the motion of the body.

What other forces are acting on the cart besides that exerted by the rubber band? Include all vertical and horizontal forces. Indicate these forces on a diagram.

● ∿∿∿∿∿∿∿∿∿∿∿∿∿∿∿∿∿∿∿∿∿∿∿∿∿∿∿∿∿∿∿∿∿∿∿

Expt. #36   ACCELERATION AND THE UNBALANCED FORCE

From the last experiment we found that a constant unbalanced force produces a constant acceleration, or that the same change in velocity takes place in equal intervals of time. The greater the time interval for which the force acts, the greater the change in velocity. In this experiment we continue the study of dynamics.

Purpose   To study the effect of different unbalanced forces on the acceleration of a body of constant mass.

Apparatus   As in Experiment 35.

Method   1. Practice pulling a cart loaded with 4 bricks along the runway using a constant force as in the previous experiment. Practice stopping the cart before it hits the bumper. Start with 1 rubber band stretched sufficiently to cause the cart, when released, to gather speed slowly as it moves across the runway. Record this stretch and use it with 2, 3 and 4 rubber bands stretched in parallel later in the experiment. The rubber loops to be connected in parallel should have the same initial length and undergo the same stretch with a given force.

2. Pass a paper tape, about the length of the runway, through the timer attaching it to the cart loaded with 4 bricks. Attach 1 rubber loop to the cart, stretching it to the extent practiced above. Release the cart. Label the resulting tape "1-loop."

118

3. Repeat the procedure, making tapes for 2, 3 and 4 loops connected in parallel and stretched to the same extent as with 1 loop. Label the tapes "2-loop," "3-loop" and "4-loop," respectively.

4. Mark the tapes off into convenient time intervals. Plot a velocity-time graph for each tape on the same graph paper and from this determine the average acceleration for the various loops. Make use of the table provided for any measurements you require for the above analysis.

Table I

Tape	1-loop		2-loop		3-loop		4-loop	
Time								

Table II

Force (number of loops)	Acceleration
1	
2	
3	
4	

5. (a) Plot a graph of force versus acceleration. Describe the graph. In what way is the acceleration of a body related to the force applied? Write a variation statement describing this relationship.

(b) Determine the slope of the graph, including units.

(c) Keeping Galileo's ideas in mind, where should the graph pass? Where does it pass? Explain.

6. Determine the acceleration the 4-brick cart would undergo if 6 parallel rubber loops were stretched to the extent used in this experiment.

Expt. #37   ACCELERATION AND INERTIAL MASS

Introduction   From the previous experiment we found that acceleration was directly proportional to the unbalanced force for a body of constant mass. What result will a change in the quantity of matter have on the motion of a body under the influence of a constant force? Using dynamics, is there any way of measuring the quantity of matter in an object?

Purpose   To study the effect of a change in mass on the acceleration of a body when a constant force is applied.

Apparatus   As in Experiment 35.

Method   1. Make 4 paper tapes to record the effect of the quantity of matter on the motion of the cart under the influence of a constant force of 2 loops. Begin with 4 bricks on the cart, removing a brick each time a new tape is made. The rubber band should be stretched sufficiently to cause the 4-brick cart, when released, to gather speed slowly as it moves along the runway.

2. Analyze the tapes to find the relationship between acceleration and mass. Make use of the table to record any measurements required.

Tape	1-brick		2-brick		3-brick		4-brick	
Time								

3. Apply graphical techniques to the data in the table to determine the relationship between acceleration and the quantity of matter in an object. Summarize the graphical procedure used and the conclusions reached below.

4. Calculate the values of force/acceleration using the force as 2 rubber bands. Plot a graph of force/acceleration against the mass. Describe the graph. In what way is F/a related to the mass (m)?

5. Inertial mass is the amount of matter in an object compared to a standard object, measured by comparing their accelerations. Determine the inertial mass of the cart in units of bricks by referring to the above graph. Indicate your reasoning.

6. Place your physics text along with 2 bricks on the cart. Accelerate it using the 2 rubber bands stretched to the same extent as before. Determine the mass of the text in bricks. Show your work and reasoning below. Cross-check this inertial mass by measuring the gravitational mass of the book in bricks with the aid of the simple meter stick balance studied earlier.

7. Explain a procedure you could use to determine the force exerted (in Newtons) by one rubber band at a given stretch.

Expt. #38   INERTIAL AND GRAVITATIONAL MASS

Introduction   How can the mass of a chunk of matter be determined when it is out in space beyond the gravitational field of any planet? Gravitational mass is measured, using an equal arm balance, by balancing the pull of gravity on the unknown mass against the pull of gravity on the standard mass. This will not work, however, if the pull of gravity is zero. The purpose of this experiment is to determine a way of measuring mass at any position in the universe.

Purpose   To study the differences between gravitational and inertial mass.

Apparatus

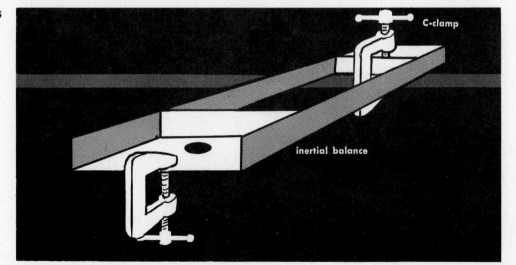

1. Attach the inertial balance to the edge of the lab table in the horizontal **Method**
   position as shown. Clamp a 3-inch C-clamp to the midpoint of the movable
   platform. Carefully pull aside the movable platform *no more than 3 cm*
   from its rest position, and release. Count in time with the vibrations as they
   occur.

2. Pull the platform aside approximately 3 cm and release. Using a stop watch,
   determine the time for 25 complete vibrations. Repeat, but this time use
   an amplitude of 1.5 cm. Repeat each of the above procedures 3 times and
   complete the table.

Amplitude	Number of vibrations	Time (sec)	Frequency	Period	Average period
3 cm					
1.5 cm					

How do the average periods of the 3 cm and the 1.5 cm amplitude vibrations compare?

What effect does changing the amplitude of the vibrations have on the:

(i) frequency?

(ii) period of the inertial balance?

3. Clamp a second 3-inch C-clamp to the midpoint of the movable platform.
   What change have you made in the gravitational mass of the platform?

Pull the platform aside about 3 cm and release. Determine the period of
the platform.

By referring to the results of Part 2, what effect does an increase in mass
have on the period of the inertial balance?

What effect does an increase in the mass have on the acceleration of the platform when the platform is pulled aside about 3 cm and released?

What should happen to the acceleration, according to Newton's Law of Motion, as the mass is increased but all other variables remain constant?

4. Remove the two 3-inch C-clamps. Attach a unit mass (one 2-inch C-clamp). Using an amplitude no greater than 3 cm, determine the time for 25 vibrations. Attach a second unit mass. Determine the time for 25 vibrations. Repeat this procedure but use, 3, 4, 5 and 6 unit masses. Enter all results in the table.

Number of attached masses	Time for 25 vibrations	Time for 1 vibration	Period
1			
2			
3			
4			
5			
6			

5. (a) Use the graphical approach to determine if there is a relationship between the mass of the object on the balance and the period of the balance by plotting a period-mass graph.

Describe the graph. Is it a straight line or a curve? If curved, what relationship might exist?

(b) Plot a graph of the period of vibration as a function of the square root of the mass. Is this a straight line? If so, determine the equation for the relationship including the numerical value of the constant. Show how you obtained the numerical value.

6. Insert the lower end of the 3-inch C-clamp through the slot in the platform and clamp in an upright position with the open end of the C facing the end of the slotted platform connected to the vibrating metal strips. Determine the time for 25 vibrations of the inertial balance and the period of the vibration.

Refer to the graph in Part 5 (a) to determine the mass of the 3-inch C-clamp in terms of unit masses.

What name is given to this method of using the graph in obtaining information?

Using the equation developed in Part 5 (b), find the mass of the C-clamp in "unit masses." Show your work.

7. Using the triple beam balance, determine the mass in grams of each of the unit masses (2-inch C-clamps).

Unit mass	1	2	3	4	5	6	Average
Mass (g)							

To within what per cent do they have the same gravitational mass?

Using the average gravitational mass from above, determine the mass in grams of the 3-inch C-clamp. Show your reasoning using complete statements.

8. Place the 3-inch C-clamp on the triple beam balance and determine its gravitational mass in grams.

What is the percentage error of your predicted value compared to the value found using the triple beam balance. Show your calculations.

What relationship seems to exist between inertial and gravitational mass?

Do inertial and gravitational mass need to have the same units?

Could the inertial mass of an object be determined where there is no gravitational field? If so, what equipment would be required?

9. Attach four 2-inch C-clamps (unit masses) to the balance. Determine the period of the balance in the horizontal position. Clamp the balance in the vertical plane with the vibrating strips facing up. Determine the period.

Clamp the balance with the vibrating strips facing down and determine the period. Does gravity affect the inertial balance in a vertical position? Discuss.

10. Compare inertial and gravitational mass using the following table. Discuss briefly.

Questions	Gravitational mass	Inertial mass
How is it measured?		
Does the standard need to be with the unknown?		
Is motion necessary for the measurement of this mass?		
Does the measurement require the presence of a gravitational field?		

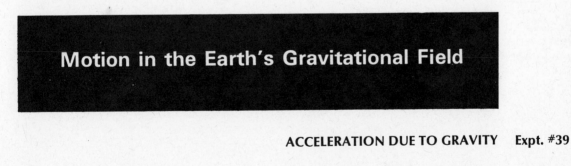

Motion in the Earth's Gravitational Field

ACCELERATION DUE TO GRAVITY **Expt. #39**

When a stone is dropped from the edge of a bridge it accelerates toward the water. This acceleration is of great importance to the study of projectile motion. What is the acceleration due to gravity? Does it vary from mass to mass? **Introduction**

To measure the acceleration of objects of different mass under free fall. **Purpose** 127

Method

1. Position the electric timer at a height of about 2 m above the floor either by clamping it to a long retort stand or by holding it in your hands. Attach a 2 m length of tape to a 1 kg mass. Activate the timer and drop the 1 kg mass. If a cushion is not available to soften the landing, have your partner catch the mass, but be careful. Label this tape "1 kg mass."

2. Repeat the procedure using a small bag of sand of different mass. Label this tape "other mass."

3. Determine the period of the electric timer as accurately as possible. Cross-check your answer with the aid of a hand stroboscope and stop watch, if you have time.

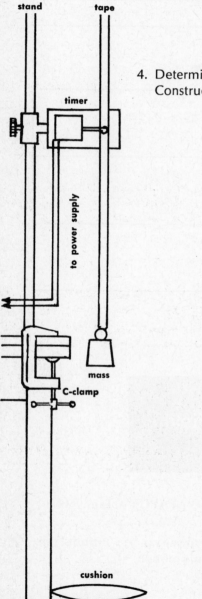

4. Determine the acceleration of the 1 kg mass and the bag of sand in cm/sec². Construct a table to show the procedure used in analyzing the tapes.

5. The correct acceleration value is approximately 980 cm/sec². Calculate the percentage difference for each of the masses. List some factors that may have contributed to this difference. Were the bodies in free fall? Discuss.

6. Why did we choose relatively large masses rather than small ones for this experiment? Discuss.

7. Can the force of gravity be used as the standard force for measuring the inertial mass of an object in terms of a standard mass? Discuss.

8. A balloon descends with a constant velocity. From it is dropped a steel sphere which takes 6 sec to reach the ground. As this sphere strikes the ground, another sphere, twice the mass of the first one, is dropped from the balloon. This sphere takes 5 sec to reach the ground. What was the height of the balloon at the instant the first sphere was released? With what speed was the balloon descending?

Expt. #40 NEWTON'S LAW FOR PROJECTILE MOTION

Introduction We have found that the force of gravity acting on a dropped object causes it to accelerate. The direction of the force is in the same direction as the velocity. Is the acceleration due to gravity affected if the body is projected horizontally with some initial velocity?

Purpose To test the validity of Newton's Law when the force is constant but not in the same direction as the initial velocity of a body.

Information The diagram below is an imaginary stroboscopic photograph of 2 billiard balls released simultaneously from the same point. One ball is allowed to fall freely while the other is projected horizontally. The light flashes at 1/30 second intervals. Each square of the grid in the background is equivalent to 10 cm. A measured distance on the diagram of 1 cm represents an actual distance of 1.55 cm.

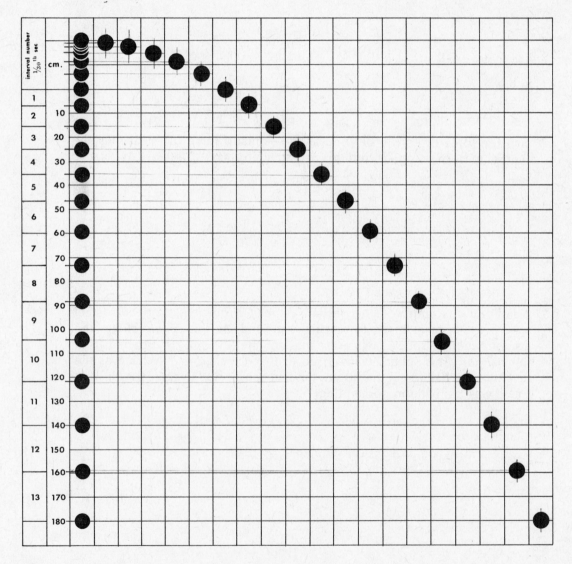

Method 1. Analyze the motion of the *dropped* ball using a cm ruler. Measure to the nearest mm. Determine the average vertical acceleration of the ball in m/sec². Summarize your calculations by constructing a suitable table in the space on page 131.

2. Analyze the motion of the projected ball by considering it to have two motions—a vertical motion and a horizontal motion—which you can consider separately.

   (a) Draw short vertical lines through the center of each image. Measure the horizontal distance travelled in each interval of 1/30 second. How do the values compare? Determine the horizontal velocity of the ball. Does the ball have any horizontal acceleration? Should it? Discuss.

(b) To analyze the vertical motion, draw a horizontal line through each image and extend toward the images of the dropped ball. How do the vertical accelerations of the 2 billiard balls compare? Discuss.

Same.

The masses of the two billiard balls are identical. Compare the magnitude and direction of the forces acting on the two billiard balls.

Same.

Does the horizontal motion of the projected ball affect its vertical acceleration? Discuss.

No.

3. A bullet is fired horizontally from a position 4 m above a level plane with a velocity of 100 m/sec. At the same time a billiard ball is dropped from this position. Which object will hit the ground first? Discuss.

Should hit ground at same time.

4. A boy wishes to throw a ball from a position 30 m away from the base of a cliff 80 m high into a horizontal pipe of about the ball's diameter. The pipe is situated at the top of the cliff. Assuming the acceleration due to gravity is 10 m/sec², determine:

Put negative sign

(i) the vertical velocity the boy must give the ball

$$a = -g$$
$$v = -gt$$
$$d = \frac{1}{2}gt^2$$

$$80 = 5t^2$$
$$t^2 = 16$$
$$t = 4 \text{ sec}$$

$$v = -(-10)(4)$$
$$= 40 \text{ m/sec}.$$

(ii) the horizontal velocity the ball must be given

$$a = 0$$
$$v = c$$
$$d = ct$$
$$30 = 4c$$
$$c = \frac{30}{4} = \frac{15}{2} = 7.5 \text{ m/sec}.$$

(iii) the resultant velocity the ball must be given to achieve the objective

$v^2 = 40^2 + (7.5)^2$

$= 1600 + \left(\frac{15}{2}\right)^2 = 1600 + \frac{225}{4}$

$= 1600 + 56.25 = 1656.25$

$v \simeq 40.7$ m/sec.   Find θ from Sine tables.

40

$\bar{v}$

θ

7.5

5. A large balloon, released at the earth's surface, accelerates uniformly up-
wards. One minute after release a flare is fired with a horizontal velocity of
2 m/sec. An observer on the ground finds the flare strikes the ground 34 m
from the point of release of the balloon. Determine:

(i) the acceleration of the balloon

$V_x = 2$ m/sec
$d = V_x t$
$34 = 2t$
$t = 17$ sec.

(ii) the height of the balloon when the flare is fired

(iii) the height of the balloon when the flare hits the ground

CENTRIPETAL FORCE AND FREQUENCY   Expt. #41

Acceleration is defined as the rate of change of velocity. The velocity of a body
changes if either its speed or its direction changes. Since the direction of the
velocity vector changes when a body moves in a circle at constant speed, it is
accelerating and, according to Newton's Law, force is required to produce this
acceleration. The force acting on a body moving in a circle causing this
acceleration is called the centripetal force.   **Introduction**

To study the relationship between the centripetal force (*F*) and the frequency
of revolution (*f*) of a body moving in a circular orbit of constant radius.   **Purpose**

mass of 1 alligator clip = mass of 1 washer   **Apparatus**

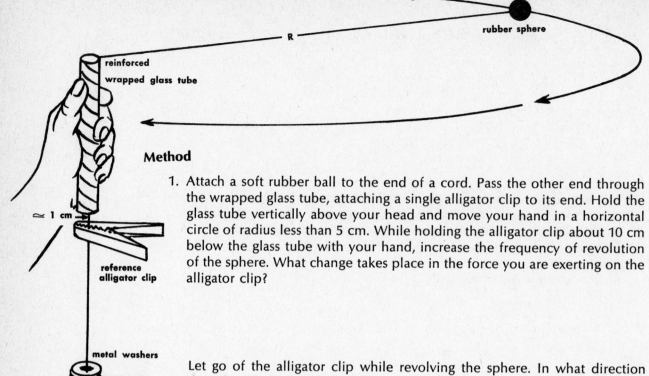

Method

1. Attach a soft rubber ball to the end of a cord. Pass the other end through the wrapped glass tube, attaching a single alligator clip to its end. Hold the glass tube vertically above your head and move your hand in a horizontal circle of radius less than 5 cm. While holding the alligator clip about 10 cm below the glass tube with your hand, increase the frequency of revolution of the sphere. What change takes place in the force you are exerting on the alligator clip?

   Let go of the alligator clip while revolving the sphere. In what direction does the whirling rubber sphere tend to move relative to the arc of a circle?

2. With a single rubber ball attached, pull the cord through the glass until the center of the ball will rotate in an orbit of radius 100 cm. Attach an alligator clip, equivalent in weight to one washer, to the cord just below the glass tube. Hang 4 washers on the string using another alligator clip to support them. The total weight on the end of the string away from the ball is equivalent to 6 units of force.

3. Swing the upper end of the glass tube in an orbit of radius less than 3 cm, increasing the frequency until the cord moves up through the tube. Maintain the frequency which keeps the upper alligator clip about 1 cm below the bottom of the glass tube. Determine the time for 20 revolutions of the ball and record.

Number of unit forces F	Time for 20 revolutions	Frequency f (rev/sec)	

4. Repeat this procedure adding 4 washers each time until a total of 28 washers and 2 alligator clips, or 30 units of force, are on the bottom of the cord. Record the time for 20 revolutions in each case.

5. Use graphical techniques to determine the relationship between force and frequency. Describe clearly the procedure used and the conclusions reached.

Write the equation for this relationship by calculating the constant of proportionality.

6. By using this equation, determine the centripetal force required to maintain one rubber ball in the same radius of orbit as used in this experiment when the orbiting body has a frequency of 5 rev/sec. Show all calculations.

~~~~~~ ●

CENTRIPETAL FORCE—MASS AND RADIUS   Expt. #42

From the previous experiment we found that the centripetal force (F) was **Introduction** directly proportional to the square of the frequency of revolution (f) provided the radius of orbit and mass were kept constant. To get a more complete picture, we should test the effect of mass and radius of orbit on the centripetal force.

To determine the relationship between centripetal force, the mass and the **Purpose** radius of orbit of an object moving in a circular path.

Apparatus As in Experiment 41.

Part I **Dependence on Mass**

Method 1. Attach a single rubber ball to one end of the cord and 6 unit forces (4 washers and 2 alligator clips) to the other end. Whirl the rubber ball as in the previous experiment, increasing the whirling frequency until the upper alligator clip moves to within 1 cm of the lower end of the glass tube. The radius of orbit should now be 100 cm. Have your partner record the time for 20 revolutions of the ball.

Attach 2 rubber balls to one end of the cord and 12 unit forces (10 washers and 2 alligator clips) to the other end. Again whirl the balls using the radius of 100 cm and vary the frequency until the alligator clip moves up to within 1 cm of the glass tube. Have your partner record the time for 20 revolutions.

Number of unit forces	Number of whirling masses	Time for 20 revolutions (sec)	Frequency (rev/sec)
	1		
	2		

2. Calculate the frequency for each case. How do they compare? What is the dependence of the centripetal force on the revolving mass when the frequency and radius are kept constant? Is this in accord with Newton's Law of Motion? Explain.

Part II **Dependence on Radius**

Method 1. Attach 12 unit forces (10 washers and 2 alligator clips) to one end of the cord and 1 rubber ball to the other end. Place the alligator clip so that when it is 1 cm from the bottom of the glass rod, the radius of the circle followed by the ball is about 0.50 m. Revolve the glass tube until the alligator clip takes the desired position. Record the time for 20 revolutions and from this calculate the frequency and frequency^2.

2. Repeat this procedure placing the alligator clip so that the radius of the circle becomes 0.75 m, 1.00 m, and 1.25 m respectively. Record the values for frequency in the table.

Radius	Number of revolutions	Time	Frequency	Frequency^2
0.50 m				
0.75 m				
1.00 m				
1.25 m				

3. We established in the previous experiment that the force (F) varies directly as the frequency^2 (f^2) for a constant radius. We know the graph of this relationship passes through the origin. Therefore, we need only one other point for each graph. Plot a graph for f^2 against the constant force of 10 washers for different radii. Label these graphs as to radius. Draw a line parallel to the force axis, cutting each of the above graphs. By interpolation, find for each radius the force required if the frequency was kept constant.

Radius	Force
0.50 m	
0.75 m	
1.00 m	
1.25 m	

4. Plot a graph of force (F) in unit forces against radius (R) in m. How does F vary with R?

5. What is the dependence of the centripetal force on the mass, the radius and the frequency?

When 1 rubber ball is whirled in a circle of radius 1 m at a frequency of 2 rev/sec, a force of 10 units is required. What force will be required to rotate 2 rubber balls in a circle of radius 2 m at a frequency of 4 rev/sec? Show all calculations.

FRAMES OF REFERENCE—FICTITIOUS FORCES **Expt. #43**

Introduction

Imagine that you are standing at the center of a platform located in the center of a room, and that the platform is rotating at a uniform speed. View the various objects not on the platform and imagine yourself at rest. If you are turning clockwise with reference to the ground a picture on the wall will appear to rotate counter clockwise in a circular path. From earlier study, recall that motion in a circular path, at constant speed, is a type of non-uniform acceleration. But accelerated motion requires an unbalanced external force. The picture must therefore have a force acting on it causing this accelerated motion with reference to yourself. You are an accelerated frame of reference since you are undergoing the circular motion. In order to explain the apparent motion of objects not on your frame of reference, you must use a fictitious force in order to satisfy Newton's Law. Is this always the case? In this experiment we are going to pursue this study.

Purpose To study the motion of objects using non-accelerated and accelerated frames of reference.

Information 1. A man is crouching on a railway flatcar which is moving east (E) with a constant velocity of 10 m/sec. While facing in the direction of the train's motion, he projects an air puck forward away from himself with a velocity of 12 m/sec along the floor of the flatcar. A man standing at rest on the ground watches the motions. Complete the following table.

Time (sec)	Train's motion (reference—ground)		Puck's motion (reference—man on ground)			Puck's motion (reference—train)		
	Velocity (m/sec) E	Position (m) E	Velocity (m/sec) E	Position (m) E	Acceleration (m/sec²) E	Velocity (m/sec) E	Position (m) E	Acceleration (m/sec²) E
0								
1								
2								
3								
4								
5								
6								

Is any body in the system undergoing accelerated motion? Does it matter what body is used as reference for the motion? Discuss. Was any fictitious force required to explain the motion of any body in the system?

2. A man is crouching on a railway flatcar initially at rest. As it starts to accelerate at 4 m/sec² E, the man projects the air puck forward away from himself in the direction of the train's motion with a velocity of 12 m/sec E. A man standing at rest on the ground observes the motion. Fill in the following table.

Time (sec)	Train's motion (reference—ground)		Puck's motion (reference—man on ground)			Puck's motion (reference—train)		
	Velocity (m/sec) E	Position (m) E	Velocity (m/sec) E	Position (m) E	Acceleration (m/sec²) E	Velocity (m/sec) E	Position (m) E	Acceleration (m/sec²) E
0								
1								
2								
3								
4								
5								
6								

(a) What kind of motion does the puck have with reference to the man on the ground?

(b) What kind of motion does the puck appear to have when the train is used as the reference? What kind of motion is the train undergoing?

(c) If the man on the train takes himself as reference, what kind of motion does he think the puck is undergoing? In order to account for this motion and make Newton's Law hold true in his frame of reference, what must be introduced?

3. The following diagram shows the motion of a motorcycle travelling with uniform velocity, and a police car travelling with uniform acceleration. The motion of both vehicles is observed by a stationary observer on the earth's frame of reference. The successive positions of the vehicles are indicated at equal time intervals. P represents the police car accelerating north and M represents the motorcycle moving due northwest at a constant velocity.

(a) Draw the vectors representing the position of the motorcycle with reference to the police car at various times on the diagram.

(b) In the police car frame of reference the car must be considered to be stationary. The earth and the motorcycle move with respect to the "stationary" police car. To determine the motion of the motorcycle in the police car's frame of reference, plot the successive positions of the motorcycle using the police car (P) as the reference position.

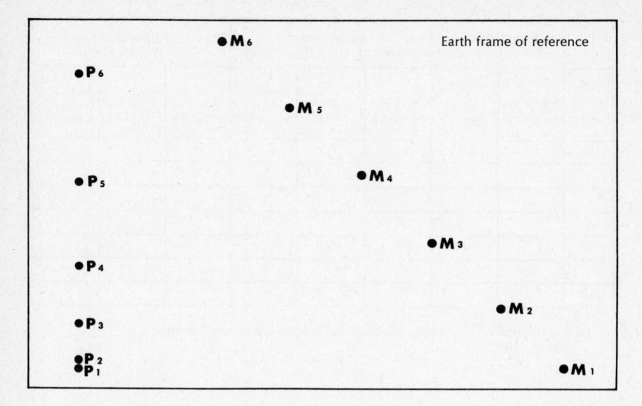

Police car frame of reference

●P

(c) Determine the change in velocity of the motorcycle as seen from the policeman's point of view in the police car's frame of reference, by determining the change in position per unit time and hence the average velocity. Subtract these average velocities to determine the change in velocity. Show your work in the space above. Since there is a change in velocity, an acceleration is occurring. Indicate the direction of the fictitious force that must be acting on the motorcycle, according to the policeman, to cause this acceleration.

4. An observer standing on a tower high above the ground watches a bird flying past a rotating merry-go-round. The successive positions of the bird and a second person on the merry-go-round are indicated on the following diagram. At the point M at the bottom of the page, construct the path of the bird's flight as seen by the person with the merry-go-round frame of reference.

(a) What name is given to the curve you have drawn with the merry-go-round frame of reference?

(b) In order to account for the motion of the bird using the merry-go-round frame of reference, what must be introduced to satisfy Newton's Law?

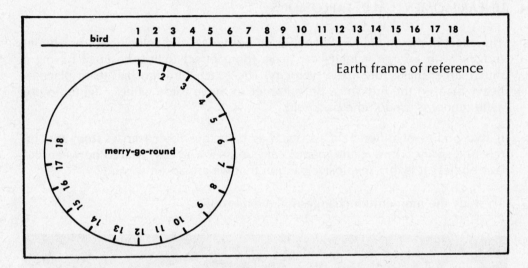

Merry-go-round frame of reference

• M

Momentum and Conservation of Momentum

Expt. #44   **LINEAR MOMENTUM IN EXPLOSIONS**

Introduction   The effect of moving objects depends on both mass and velocity. A small bullet moving with a large velocity can have more effect than a baseball having a much larger mass but smaller velocity. The coach of a football team places a heavy man on the line since he is harder to move aside while a lighter, more agile runner is used in the backfield.

If two bodies of different mass, such as carts, are forced apart from rest by released springs, how is the momentum (mass × velocity) shared between the two bodies? It is this "explosive" action that we are about to study.

Purpose   To study the momentum changes in an explosion.

Apparatus

Method   1. Examine the cart, noting the position of the spring and the method of loading and releasing it. *(The spring must not be cocked without first being safely attached to the cart. Do not point the spring at anyone when releasing it.)* Clamp the two bumpers to the table, 1.5 m apart. Cock the spring of one cart. Place it on the table. Release the spring with the cart at rest. What do you observe?

Repeat the procedure with 1, 2 and 3 bricks on the cart. How does the horizontal momentum before the spring is released compare with that after?

142

2. Place a single brick on each of 2 carts which in turn are placed back to back so that when the spring of one is released it will push on the other. Release the spring. What happens?

What do you observe with 2 bricks on one cart and 1 on the other?

Place 2 bricks on each cart and release the spring. How do the results in this case compare with both of the above results?

Compare the force exerted on each cart by the spring.

When comparing the masses, which cart attains the greater velocity from the force?

Compare the momenta of the two carts after the spring is released.

3. The explosions can be studied quantitatively by measuring the mass and velocity of the carts before and after the explosion. A simple way to compare velocities is to compare the distance travelled at constant velocity in equal time intervals. Since *displacement = constant velocity × time*, therefore *displacement ∝ constant velocity*, provided the time is kept constant.

Arrange to have the carts travel for the same time after the explosion by adjusting the starting position before the explosion until each cart hits the bumper at the same instant and only one bang is heard. For example, if the 2 equal-massed carts are exploded apart from the midpoint between the 2 bumpers and hit the bumpers at the same time, they must have had the same speed after the explosion.

If one cart hits the bumper before the other, arrange the starting position to have it travel a greater distance before impact until one impact is heard. Measure the distances and use these as an indication of the velocities after the explosion. Use this method of adjusting for equal times in the following procedure.

143

4. Label one cart 1 and the other 2. Place 1 brick on each cart and adjust for equal time as suggested. Measure d_1 and d_2 and m_1 and m_2 (in bricks). Repeat this using the number of bricks indicated in the table below. Remember that the cart has an appreciable mass.

m_1	$\vec{d_1}$	m_2	$\vec{d_2}$	$m_1\vec{d_1}$	$m_2\vec{d_2}$	$\dfrac{m_1\vec{d_1}}{m_2\vec{d_2}}$
1-brick		1-brick				
2-brick		1-brick				
1-brick		2-brick				
2-brick		3-brick				
2-brick		4-brick				
3-brick		4-brick				

How does the direction of $\vec{d_1}$ compare to $\vec{d_2}$?

How will you indicate this in your ratio?

What was the total momentum before the explosion?

What was the total momentum after the explosion ($m_1\vec{d_1} + m_2\vec{d_2}$)?

What can you conclude? What kind of quantity is momentum?

Note: $m_1\vec{d_1}$ is only used to compare momenta. It is not the true momentum.

5. A 500 kg log AB, 10 m long, is floating freely with end A touching a stationary post. A 90 kg lumberjack is standing on the log 1.0 m from end B. He walks to a point 1.0 m from end A. How far is he from the post, neglecting the resistance of the water to the log's motion.

LINEAR MOMENTUM IN A COLLISION

Expt. #45

Introduction

In the previous experiment we studied momentum when an explosion occurred between two stationary objects. Is momentum conserved when a collision rather than an explosion takes place?

Purpose

To study the momentum changes occurring when a moving cart of variable mass encounters a stationary cart of constant mass.

Apparatus

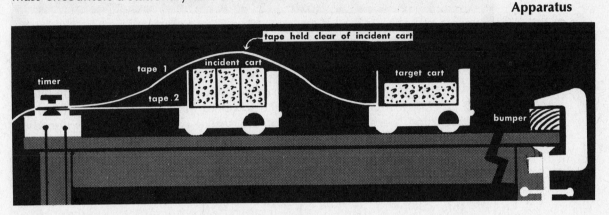

Method

1. Set up the apparatus as shown in the diagram with 1 brick on the target cart and 2 bricks on the incident cart. Attach paper tapes to both carts, threading them through the same timer using a carbon paper disc for each. Suspend the tape from the target cart out of the way of the incident cart and prevent it from moving through the timer until the collision takes place. Place the incident cart about 0.75 m closer to the timer than the target cart. No spring plungers should be used.

2. Activate the timer and give the incident cart a big push toward the target cart. Label the resulting tapes "Case A – incident cart and 2 bricks," and "Case A – target cart and 1 brick."

3. Repeat the procedure with the single brick on the target cart, but with 3 and then 4 bricks on the incident cart. Label the tapes "Case B" and "Case C," respectively. Each member of the experimental group should analyze only one pair of tapes.

4. Calibrate the timer in the following way. Place a new tape in the timer, making sure the timer has the same frequency as before. Activate the timer, pulling the tape through for a measured time. Count the number of tick marks on the tape in this time. From this, calculate the time between ticks in seconds.

5. Each member of the group must now analyze one pair of tapes. Each tape of the incident cart will look to some degree as illustrated below.

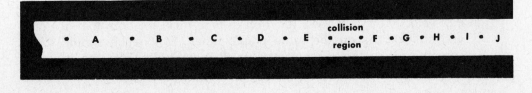

By inspection, locate the collision region on each of the incident tapes and mark it as shown. Count off 5 ticks on each side of the collision region, labelling these A to J, as shown. Measure the distance travelled in each tick in cm and record in the table. From the distance travelled, calculate the average speed for each interval in cm/tick.

Each target cart tape will look to some degree as illustrated below. By inspection locate the collision region.

Mark the tape off in tick intervals from the collision region using the letters F, G, H, I, J. Measure the distance travelled in each interval and tabulate. Determine the average speed of the struck cart during each interval in cm/tick and tabulate.

	Incident cart		Target cart	
Interval	Distance (cm)	Average speed (cm/tick)	Distance (cm)	Average speed (cm/tick)
A				
B				
C				
D				
E				
F				
G				
H				
I				
J				

Mass of incident cart and load (in bricks)	Mass of target cart and load (in bricks)	1 brick = ———— kg

6. Find the mass of each cart plus its load (in bricks) before collision. Also determine the mass of one brick in kg and record. The simple meter stick balance studied in Experiment 6 can be used to determine these masses. Tabulate the results in the appropriate space above.

7. (a) Plot velocity (cm/tick) as a function of time (tick) for both the incident and struck carts on the same graph paper. Your result should look something like the diagram shown. Remember to plot the average velocity at half time in the tick interval.

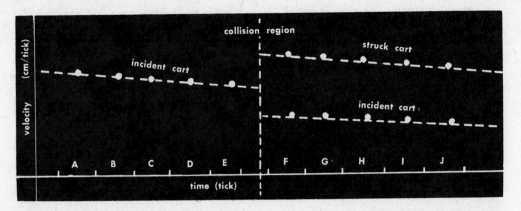

(b) By studying your partner's tapes and graphs, compare the velocity change when the mass of the loaded cart is greater, with the change when the mass is less.

8. By extrapolating the plotted lines for both the incident and target carts to the collision region on the speed-time graph, determine:

(i) the speed of the incident cart immediately preceding the collision

(ii) the speed of the incident cart immediately following the collision

(iii) the speed of the target cart immediately following the collision

9. Use the speed from Part 8 and the mass from Part 6 to determine the total momenta of the system before and after the collision (in bricks-cm/tick). Show your calculations below.

Before collision.	After collision.

Compare the total momentum of the system before and after the collision.

Before collision.	After collision.

10. Determine the change in momentum of the incident cart by using its change in speed and mass (in brick-cm/tick).

Determine the change in momentum of the struck cart (in brick-cm/tick). Compare the change in momentum of the incident cart with that of the struck cart.

11. (a) In order to determine the impulse applied to a body which causes the change in momentum, we can consider the force applied and the time for which this force is applied. By examining the incident tapes, approximately how long did the collision last in ticks? in seconds?

(b) What was the change in momentum (in brick-cm/tick) of

(i) the incident cart?

(ii) the struck cart?

By using suitable conversion factors, determine these changes in momenta in kg-m/sec.

(c) Using the time determined in (a) and the total change in momentum from (b), determine the horizontal force applied by:

(i) the incident cart on the target cart in Newtons

(ii) the target cart on the incident cart in Newtons

Compare the magnitude and direction of these forces.

12. A cart of mass 2 kg is carrying 1 kg of sand in a funnel at the back. When the cart is moving with a speed of 0.5 m/sec, the bottom of the funnel opens releasing the sand. Will this affect the motion of the cart? Discuss.

13. A cart of mass 2 kg, moving with a velocity of 0.5 m/sec E, collides head-on with a stationary cart of mass 4 kg. Calculate the velocity of the incident cart after the collision, if the struck cart attains a velocity of .75 m/sec E. Account for the negative sign of this velocity. Do you think the results obtained are valid for a real situation? Discuss.

14. A strong wagon of mass 15 kg, moving with a velocity of 10 m/sec E, passes beneath a tree. A monkey of mass 10 kg drops from a tree limb 5 m above the ground landing on the wagon. Determine the velocity of the wagon and monkey after the monkey lands on it.

Expt. #46   **TWO DIMENSIONAL MOMENTUM—COLLISIONS BETWEEN EQUAL MASSES**

Introduction   From previous experiments with colliding and exploding bodies, we derived the Principle of Conservation of Momentum for interactions in one dimension. Does this Principle apply when off-centered collisions occur causing the bodies to move in different directions after the interaction?

To determine the momenta of the bodies before and after the collision, it is necessary to know their masses and velocities, since momentum is the product of mass and velocity. However, if the bodies move with a constant velocity for the same time interval, we can use the displacement travelled to represent velocity, since

$$displacement = constant\ velocity \times time$$

therefore,

$$displacement \propto constant\ velocity\ \text{(providing the time is kept constant)}$$

To compare the momenta before and after a collision, we could use the product of mass and displacement. We can simplify the analysis by studying collisions of bodies of equal masses. Momenta can then be compared by comparing displacement only.

From the study of projectile motion we know that the time for an object projected horizontally to hit the floor is independent of the horizontal velocity. If air resistance is negligible, the horizontal component of a projectile's velocity remains constant, and the horizontal displacement travelled from the projected point to the landing point is directly proportional to the momentum of the body since the bodies travel for the same time before hitting the floor.

Purpose   To determine if momentum is a vector quantity and if momentum is conserved in off-centered collisions.

Apparatus

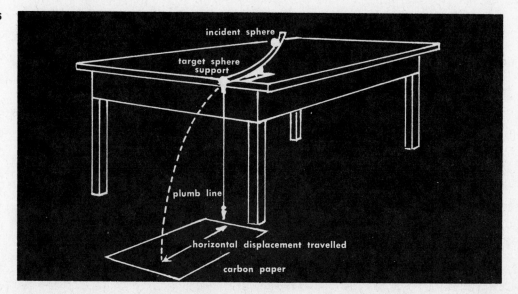

150

1. The projection velocity will be given to the incident sphere by releasing it from a point exactly 25 cm up the ruler slope. Swivel the target ball support until it is directly in line with the end of the launching ramp. Release the incident sphere from the 25 cm point on the ramp, and adjust the height of the target sphere support until the incident sphere will just clear its top.

2. Place 4 sheets of carbon paper on the floor, face up, covered by a large sheet of tracing paper. Position these so that the plumb bob suspended from the base of the target sphere support hangs directly over the middle of the one end as shown. Tape the paper in place. Mark the point directly beneath the plumb bob with an x.

3. To determine the horizontal momentum of the incident sphere before the collision, release the steel sphere from a point exactly 25 cm up the ruler about 10 times, allowing it to project freely and hit the paper each time. Draw in the vector representing the horizontal momentum before collision by joining the point x (beneath the bob) to the center of the distribution of points made as the incident sphere hit the paper. How constant was this incident momentum? Discuss.

4. Place the target sphere of equal mass on its support. Swivel this support slightly sideways to produce an off-centered collision between the incident and target spheres. Mark the point directly beneath the plumb bob S_1. Release the incident steel sphere from the 25 cm point on the ruler. Label the impact point made by the target sphere T_1 and the incident sphere I_1.

5. To produce different off-centered collisions, swivel the target sphere to different positions marking its location with an S_n. Release the target sphere from the 25 cm location each time and label the impact points of the target and incident sphere T_n and I_n, respectively. Repeat the procedure until a total of 4 off-centered collisions are recorded.

6. To draw the vector representing the momentum of the target sphere after collision, join the points S_1 and T_1.

7. Approximate on the paper the location of the incident sphere just as it hits the target sphere. Label this point O_1. Draw the vector representing the momentum of the incident sphere after impact by joining O_1 and I_1.

8. Add the vectors representing the momenta of the incident and target spheres after the collision using the head to tail method, by placing the tail of the target sphere vector at the head of the incident sphere vector. Compare their vector sum with the length and direction of the vector representing the total momentum of the incident sphere before the collision. Is momentum conserved in a two-dimensional collision? Discuss.

9. Check your observations by analyzing the second, third and fourth collisions. What do you conclude?

10. Measure the magnitude only of the vectors representing the momenta after the collision. Add these arithmetically. Is the arithmetic sum equal to the length of the vector representing the total momentum before collision? What type of quantity must momentum be?

11. A 21 kg rock moving east with a velocity of 5 m/sec explodes into 3 equal parts. After the explosion, part *A* travels northeast at 3 m/sec, and part *B* travels southeast at 5 m/sec. Determine the direction and velocity of part C.

●〜〜〜〜〜〜〜〜〜〜〜〜〜〜〜〜〜〜〜〜〜〜〜〜〜〜〜〜

Expt. #47   ELASTIC COLLISIONS IN TWO DIMENSIONS

Introduction   In the previous experiment we found that momentum is conserved vectorially in off-centered collisions. Does mass affect momentum? Is anything conserved besides momentum in collisions between elastic bodies such as steel spheres or glass alleys which return to their original shapes? In order to study this we will use the same apparatus as in the previous experiment. In the collision between the metal spheres, we used the horizontal displacment travelled by the projectiles to represent momenta. This is true only for bodies of equal mass. The horizontal displacement travelled is always proportional to the velocity of the projectile, since the time of travel is the same for each. We will be using these vectors as *velocity* vectors throughout this experiment.

152

To determine the relationship between mass and momentum and to determine **Purpose**
if anything other than momentum is conserved in elastic collisions.

As in Experiment 46. **Apparatus**

Method

1. Place 4 sheets of carbon paper face up on the floor, covered by a large
   sheet of tracing paper with the plumb bob suspended from the base of the
   target sphere support hanging directly over the middle of one end. Mark
   the point directly beneath the bob with an x.

2. Adjust the height of the target sphere support so that the incident sphere
   will just clear the top when released from a point 25 cm up the ruler ramp.

3. Release the incident steel sphere from a point exactly 25 cm up the ruler
   ramp a number of times, allowing it to project freely and hit the paper.
   Draw in the vector representing the horizontal velocity immediately before collision by joining the point x beneath the bob to the center of the
   distribution of points made as the incident sphere hit the paper. Measure
   its length in cm and record in Table I.

4. Place the steel target sphere of equal mass on the support. Swivel the
   support slightly sideways to produce an off-centered collision. Mark the
   point on the paper directly below the plumb bob S. Release the incident
   steel sphere from the 25 cm point. Label the impact points I_1 and T_1. Draw
   the vectors representing the velocity of the incident sphere and target
   sphere after the impact. Measure their lengths in cm and record in Table I.
   Assume the mass of each sphere is unity (one).

Let v represent velocity in cm. Let m represent mass in units. **Table I**

Before collision			After collision					
Incident sphere			Incident sphere			Target sphere		
v (cm)	v^2 (cm^2)	mv^2	v (cm)	v^2 (cm^2)	mv^2	v (cm)	v^2	mv^2

5. (a) Add the magnitude of the velocity vectors after the collision (in cm)
   and record below. Is this sum equal to the magnitude of the incident
   sphere's velocity before impact?

   (b) Determine the square of the velocities of the incident sphere before the
   collision and of the incident and target spheres after the collision, entering the results in Table I. How does the sum of the squares of the
   velocities after collision compare with the square of the velocity before
   collision? How does the sum of *mass* × *velocity*^{2} values compare after
   collision with that before? Why?

6. Repeat the experiment using the same incident metal sphere but a lighter target glass sphere of the same diameter. Use a new sheet of tracing paper and label it "unequal masses." Be sure to record the point reached by the incident sphere without a collision and the points reached by the incident and target spheres following a collision. Repeat using different off-centered conditions until 4 unequal mass collisions have occurred. Why is the sphere of greater mass used as the incident sphere?

7. Draw the vectors representing the velocity of the incident sphere before and after collision and the target sphere after collision. Measure the length in cm of these vectors and enter as velocities in Table II.

Table II

| Before collision | | | After collision | | | | | |
| Incident sphere | | | Incident sphere | | | Target sphere | | |
v	v^2	mv^2	v	v^2	mv^2	v	v^2	mv^2

8. (a) Is the sum of the velocities after the collision equal to the initial velocity of the incident sphere?

(b) Determine the square of the velocities of the incident sphere before the collision and of the incident and target spheres after the collision. How does the sum of the squares of the velocities after the collision compare with the square of the velocity before the collision?

(c) Measure the mass of a number of the steel spheres using a balance. Measure the mass of the same number of glass alleys. If you assign one metal sphere a mass of unity (one), what mass would you assign one glass alley?

Complete Table II by calculating *mass* × *velocity*^{2} for each case. How does the sum of the *mass* × *velocity*^{2} values for the spheres after collision, compare with the *mass* × *velocity*^{2} value for the incident sphere before the collision?

What is conserved in this reaction besides momentum? On which two variables does it depend? How does it depend on each?

9. Analyze one of the unequal mass collisions to check if momentum is conserved. Explain in detail how the check was performed and show the analyzed data.

10. Repeat the experiment using a spherical piece of plasticene as the target sphere and the steel sphere as the incident sphere. Is the product (mv^2) conserved? Compare the magnitude of mv^2 before with the magnitude of mv^2 after the collision. Is this an elastic collision? Refer to your text to determine the properties of an elastic collision, or perform the next experiment before answering the question completely.

Work and Kinetic Energy

Expt. #48   THE NATURE OF ELASTIC COLLISIONS

Introduction   In the previous experiment, we found that the total kinetic energy of the system was the same after as before the collision. Is kinetic energy conserved throughout the collision?

Purpose   To analyze the intermediate stages of a theoretical elastic collision between two bodies of different mass.

Apparatus

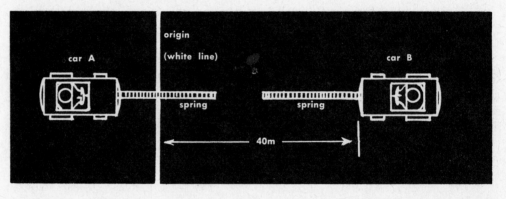

Information   A racing car A of mass 300 kg, travelling at a constant velocity of 24 m/sec eastward along a straight level racing strip, collides head-on with a stationary racing car B of mass 100 kg. Each car has an elastic spring 20 m long to cushion the collision and provide an elastic interaction. Assume that the two cars exert no force on each other until the springs touch at a separation between the cars of $d = 40$ m, and then each exerts a repulsive force of 600 Newtons on the other.

A white line across the racing strip represents both the starting point for the collision and the *origin* for our analysis. Car B is situated 40 m east of this point. Assume the collision takes place at *time* = 0, when A crosses the white line 40 m from B. The springs will compress until the separation reaches a minimum and then expand until the cars are again separated by $d = 40$ m, at which time the springs cease to exert any force and the collision is over. When the collision is over, A and B will continue to separate with velocities which remain constant.

Part I   The Mechanics of the Collision

Method   1. Determine the velocity and position of cars A and B with reference to the origin (the white line), when $t = -3, -2, -1$ and 0 seconds. Remember the collision does not occur until after $t = 0$.

2. Let direction east be positive. Immediately after $t = 0$, what is the magnitude and direction of the force:

(i) exerted by A on B

(ii) exerted by B on A

Using these forces, and the masses of the respective cars, determine the acceleration:

(i) of car B during the collision

(ii) of car A during the collision

3. Calculate the velocities car A and car B will have from $t = 1$ to $t = 6$ at successive second intervals. If Δd represents the distance travelled in each Δt of 1 second duration, calculate the respective Δd's for A and B from $t = 0$ seconds to $t = 6$ seconds. Then determine the successive positions of A and B with reference to the origin (the white line) from $t = 0$ seconds to $t = 6$ seconds. Calculate the separation (s) between A and B at each of these times. Enter all calculations in Table I.

Mechanics of colliding bodies A and B   Table I

Time (sec)	Object A			Object B			Separation s (m)
	Velocity V (m/sec)	Successive distances d (m)	Position from origin x (m)	Velocity V (m/sec)	Successive distances d (m)	Position from origin x (m)	
−3							
−2							
−1							
0							
1							
2							
3							
4							
5							
6							
7							
8							
9							

Questions   1. At $t = 0$, as the collision started, the cars were separated by 40 m.

    (a) During what interval of time was the separation decreasing? increasing?

    (b) At what time was the separation (s) at its minimum? Compare the velocities of cars A and B at this time.

    (c) When is the collision over? What is the separation of the cars at this time? What is the velocity of car A and of car B at this time? What kind of motion will the cars have following completion of the collision? Why? What is the unbalanced force acting on the cars when the collision is over?

  2. (a) How far did A move during the collision?

       What was the magnitude of the force exerted on A?

       For A only, calculate the product of force and distance moved. What sign does it have?

       What does this product represent in terms of work? energy?

       Is the energy transferred into or out of A?

    (b) How far did B move during the collision?

       What was the magnitude of the force exerted on B?

For *B* only, calculate the product of force and distance moved? What sign does it have?

What does this product represent in terms of work? energy?

Is the energy transferred into or out of *B*?

(c) Compare the energy lost by *A* with the energy gained by *B*. Account for this in terms of force and distance moved.

3. Complete Table I by determining the velocity, position and separation of *A* and *B* for $t = 7, 8$ and 9 seconds.

4. (a) Plot a position-time graph for the collision from $t = 0$ to $t = 8$ seconds. Remember that car *A* is at the origin at $t = 0$ and *B* is at $+40$ m.

   Label the separation when the collision begins and ends. Label the minimum separation region.

   (b) Observe the graph for car *A*. Describe its shape. What kind of motion is it under during the collision? after the collision? How could you tell from looking at the graph?

   (c) Observe the graph for car *B*. Describe its shape. What does this indicate about its motion:

   (i) during the collision?

   (ii) after the collision?

The Momentum of the Collision   **Part II**

Enter these calculations in Table II.

1. By using the velocities of cars *A* and *B* tabulated in Table I, determine the momentum of *A* and *B* for $t = -1$ to $t = 7$ seconds. Calculate the total momentum of the system at each of these times.   **Method**

Table II Momentum

Time (sec)	Momentum of A $\vec{P}_A$ (kg-m/sec)	Momentum of B $\vec{P}_B$ (kg-m/sec)	Total Momentum $\vec{P}_T$ (kg-m/sec)
−1			
0			
1			
2			
3			
4			
5			
6			
7			

Questions 1. (a) What is the total momentum of the system before the collision? Which body possesses it?

(b) What is the total momentum at any time during the collision? Is momentum conserved at intermediate stages of the collision? Did you expect this? Why?

Part III The Kinetic Energy of the Collision

Method Enter these calculations in Table III.

1. By using the velocities of the cars tabulated in Table I, determine the kinetic energies of A and B and the total kinetic energy of the system for $t = -1$ to $t = 7$ seconds.

Time (sec)	Kinetic energy		
	Car A (joules)	Car B (joules)	Total (joules)
−1			
0			
1			
2			
3			
4			
5			
6			
7			

Questions

1. Which car loses kinetic energy during the collision? Is all this kinetic energy transferred to the other car immediately?

2. At what time and separation is the kinetic energy of the system at its minimum? Compare the velocities of the cars when the kinetic energy is at its minimum? Where is the missing kinetic energy?

Changes in Kinetic Energy   Part IV

Enter these calculations in Table IV.   **Method**

1. Determine the change in kinetic energy of the system compared to the kinetic energy at the start of the collision for each second throughout the collision.

2. The separation when the collision began was 40 m. Calculate the change in separation compared to this initial separation, by referring to Table I, for each second during the collision.

3. Enter the force that was acting throughout the collision and calculate the product of the force and the change in separation.

161

Table IV   Changes in Kinetic Energy

Time (sec)	Total kinetic energy E_k (joules)	Change in kinetic energy ΔE_k (joules)	Change in separation ΔS (m)	Force F (Newtons)	Force × change in separation $F \Delta S$ (Newton-m)
0					
1					
2					
3					
4					
5					
6					

Questions

1. How does the product of force and the change in separation compare to the change in kinetic energy during each time interval? Write an expression which will enable you to find the change in kinetic energy of elastic systems knowing only the force of interaction and the change in separation.

2. Test the expression at intermediate stages of the collision by determining the change in kinetic energy of the system from $t = 2$ to $t = 5$ seconds, using Table III. Cross-check this using the equation involving force and change in separation. What sign did the change in separation have? Is kinetic energy lost or gained during this stage of the collision?

3. Plot a force-separation graph with force on the y axis and separation on the x axis for this collision. How could you find the change in kinetic energy of the system using this graph? Find the change in kinetic energy from $t = 2$ to $t = 5$ seconds using this graph.

Summary

Make a list of some of the properties of an elastic collision.

1.

2.

3.

4.

5.

6.

7.

~~~~~~ ●

ELASTIC COLLISIONS AND STORED ENERGY   Expt. #49

Introduction

The kinetic energy of a body of mass M moving with a speed of V is given by the equation $E_k = \frac{1}{2} MV^2$. But the average speed of a body which travels a distance Δd in a time interval Δt is given by $V = \Delta d/\Delta t$. By substituting $V = \Delta d/\Delta t$ for V in the kinetic energy equation, we obtain $E_k = \frac{1}{2}m\frac{\Delta d^2}{\Delta t^2}$. If the mass being considered is 2 kg and we measure the distance travelled every second, the expression could be simplified to

$$E_k = \frac{1}{2} \times 2\ kg \times \frac{\Delta d^2}{1\ sec^2} = \frac{1\ kg}{sec^2}\Delta d^2 = K\Delta d^2, \text{ where } K = \frac{1\ kg}{sec^2}$$

This would give us the kinetic energy in joules, provided the distances are measured in m.

Purpose

To analyze the motion of two magnets of equal mass undergoing an off-centered collision on a frictionless surface.

Information

Imagine a stroboscopic photograph of 2 circular magnets each of mass 2 kg, situated on a frictionless table. Initially, magnet A was moving and magnet B was at rest. The numbered intervals, representing times of 1 second, mark the distances travelled by each magnet during successive 2 stroboscope flashes. The flash frequency was 2 flashes per second. Assume the distances in the photograph are 1/10 actual size.

Method

Enter all results and calculations in the table.

1. Measure the distance travelled by each 2 kg magnet in a time interval of 1 second. Remember that the photograph is reduced. A measured distance of 1 cm represents an actual distance of 0.10 m.

2. Measure the separation between the two bodies at the mid-time of the 1-second intervals.

163

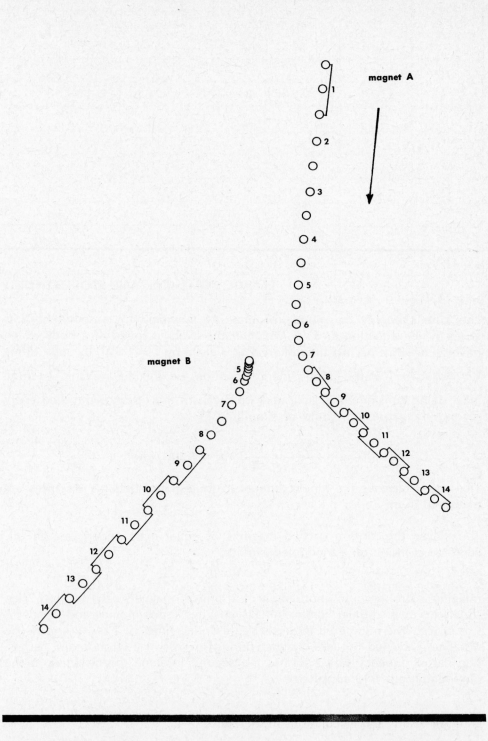

3. Calculate the kinetic energy of each body in joules at 1-second intervals using the relationship $E_k = K\Delta d^2$, where $K = 1$ kg/sec². Sum the kinetic energy of each body to obtain the total kinetic energy of the system.

4. Calculate the kinetic energy that has disappeared from the system at 1-second intervals. This is the stored energy.

Time interval (sec)	Distance travelled		Kinetic energies			Stored energy (joules)	Separation (m)
	Magnet A (m)	Magnet B (m)	Magnet A (joules)	Magnet B (joules)	Total (joules)		
1							
2							
3							
4							
5							
6							
7							
8							
9							
10							
11							
12							
13							
14							

5. Plot a graph of total kinetic energy of the system in joules versus time in seconds. Describe the graph. When is the kinetic energy at its minimum? How would you describe the separation at this time?

6. Plot graphs of:

(i) the total kinetic energy of the system versus separation

(ii) the stored energy of the system versus separation

(a) As the separation decreases, what happens to the kinetic energy of the system? As the kinetic energy decreases, describe the change in the stored energy. On what single factor does the stored energy of this system depend?

(b) Compare the kinetic energies of the system at the same separation when the magnets are coming together and going apart. Account for your observations. Would you consider this collision to be perfectly elastic?

(c) If friction is present when the bodies are moving, compare the directions of the magnetic and frictional forces as the bodies are coming together and separating. What effect would this have on the collision?

7. A moving 5 kg mass A collides elastically head-on with a stationary mass B. Masses A and B have velocities of 4 m/sec E and 5 m/sec W, respectively, after the collision. Determine:

(i) the mass of B

(ii) the velocity of A before the collision

Potential Energy

HOOKE'S LAW FOR A SPRING   **Expt. #50**

Introduction

A force is required to extend or compress an elastic spring. When the extension or compression is zero at the rest position, the force is zero. When the spring is deformed, work is done since a force acts through a displacement.

Is this force constant, or does it change as the spring is deformed to different extents? We must determine this before the work done on the spring can be calculated.

Purpose

To determine the relationship between the force applied to an elastic spring, and the extension produced.

Apparatus

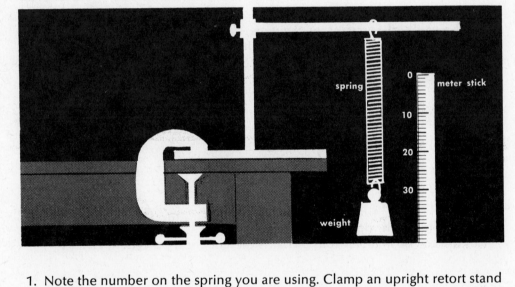

Method

1. Note the number on the spring you are using. Clamp an upright retort stand to the edge of the lab table. Suspend the elastic spring over the edge of the table from a horizontal support as shown. Record the vertical height (in m) of the lower end of the spring from the floor, in the table provided.

2. Hang a 200 g mass on its lower end and gently lower it until the spring supports the weight. Record the vertical height (in m) of the end of the spring from the floor.

3. Add more masses to the free end of the spring in steps up to a maximum amount of 1400 g. Each time a mass is added record its value and gently lower the free end to the rest position, and record the vertical height from the floor.

4. Determine the extension of the spring (in m) under the influence of the

167

various masses by subtracting the height of the free end above the floor with the mass attached from the height with no mass attached. Enter these values in the table.

5. Convert the mass attached to the end of the spring to units of kg, and then to a force (in Newtons). Use $g = 10$ Newtons/kg.

Attached mass (g)	Attached mass (kg)	Force F (Newtons)	Height from floor (m)	Extension of spring x (m)
0	0	0		0
200				

6. Plot a graph of Force (F), in Newtons, on the y axis versus extension (x), in m on the x axis. Describe the graph obtained. What relationship exists between the extension x and the force F. This relationship is Hooke's Law. Where does the graph pass?

7. From the graph, determine the extension (in m) that would be produced by a force of 11.0 Newtons. What is the graphical procedure called?

8. Determine the slope of the line on the graph and write the equation for the relationship between extension (x) and force (F). Is the graph linear throughout the entire range of forces applied?

9. Using the equation, determine the extension when a force of 11.0 Newtons is applied. Show the calculations. Compare the value obtained in Part 7 with that obtained here.

10. By using the equation, determine the extension if a force of 550 Newtons was used. What procedure would you use in order to find the answer using the graph? Do you think the answer obtained using the equation is valid? Explain.

11. Determine the work done on the spring by applying the force of 8.0 Newtons. Explain the procedure used.

    How would you find the work done on the spring for a given extension if your graph was a curve?

12. Derive an equation for the elastic potential energy stored in the spring in terms of the extension and the force constant of the spring. Notice that the y axis of the force-extension graph has units of force while the x axis has units of distance. The area under this curve then represents the work done in deforming the spring. Of what kind of figure are you finding the area?

    What is the area in terms of F and x?

    Replace F in the above result with its equivalent in terms of K and x, from Part 8.

You should now have the equation for elastic potential energy expressed in terms of x only. Write this equation below, defining each of the symbols used.

13. The force-compression graph for an elastic spring is shown below.

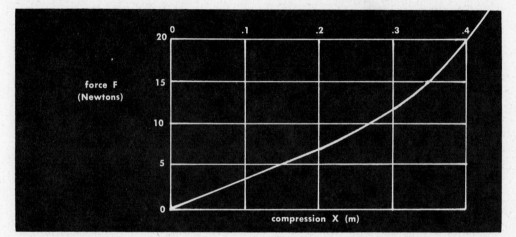

Determine:

(i) the force constant of the spring up to a compression of 0.2 m

(ii) the potential energy stored in the spring at a compression of 0.4 m

Expt. #51 CHANGES IN ELASTIC AND GRAVITATIONAL POTENTIAL ENERGY

Introduction From the last experiment you found that the deformation of an elastic body is directly proportional to the magnitude of the applied force, provided the elastic limit is not exceeded. This is Robert Hooke's Law.

When a force is applied to a spring, the work done is stored in the spring as elastic potential energy. Under zero elongation, the spring has zero elastic potential energy. If a mass is attached to a suspended spring, and the spring is released from its rest position, it vibrates. The elastic potential energy alternatively increases and decreases. When the spring is at rest at the bottom of its motion, the gravitational potential energy lost by the falling mass is stored in the spring as elastic potential energy. This energy is used to do work against the gravitational force field of the earth in raising the mass.

Purpose

To study the relationship between the elastic potential energy stored in a stretched spring and the change in gravitational potential energy of the attached mass.

Apparatus

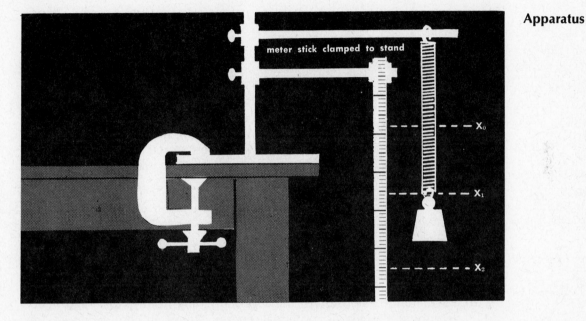

meter stick clamped to stand

x_0

x_1

x_2

Method

1. Suspend the same spring as you used in the Hooke's Law experiment over the edge of the table from a horizontal support as shown. Suspend a meter stick behind, but close to, the spring with the scale along the axis of the spring in an easily visible location. Arrange to have the zero end of the meter stick up.

2. (a) Note the reading on the meter stick directly opposite the free end of the spring under zero stretch. We will designate this as x_0.

$x_0 = $ _____ cm

Attach a one kilogram mass to the spring and gently lower it to a point exactly 20 cm below the x_0 position. Designate this point x_1. Release the mass from the x_1 position and note the maximum position to which the spring extends by placing the tip of a pencil on this point. Repeat the procedure several times until the position of maximum extension of the spring has been accurately determined. Designate this position x_2.

$x_2 = $ _____ cm

(b) Determine the distance (in m) from x_1 to x_2. Use the gravitational potential energy equation $\Delta U_g = mg\Delta x$ where

171

ΔU_g = change in gravitational potential energy in joules

m = mass in kg

g = gravitational force field in Newtons per kilogram (N/kg)

Δx = change in height in m

Assuming g is 10 N/kg, determine the loss in gravitational potential energy in joules of the mass as it falls from x_1 to x_2. Show your calculations below.

(c) Calculate the extension of the spring in going from x_0 to x_1 and determine the elastic potential energy (in joules) stored in the spring at this extension by using the elastic potential energy equation for this spring developed in the previous experiment.

(d) Calculate the extension of the spring in going from x_0 to x_2 and hence determine the elastic potential energy stored in the spring at this extension.

(e) Calculate the gain in elastic potential energy in the spring as it stretches from extension x_1 to extension x_2. Compare this to the loss in gravitational potential energy of the falling mass.

3. Repeat the procedure, but release the mass from a point exactly 25 cm below the no load position (x_0) of the spring. Record x_1 and x_2. Calculate the loss in gravitational potential energy of the falling mass and the gain

in elastic potential energy of the stretched spring. How do they compare? Show all calculations.

4. Repeat the procedure, but use a mass of 0.5 kg and release it from a point exactly 10 cm below the no load position (x_0) of the spring. Compare the loss in gravitational potential energy with the gain in elastic potential energy. Is there any appreciable energy lost from the system? Is the spring elastic?

5. (a) Attach a 0.5 kg mass to the end of the spring. Release the mass from the no load position x_0. Call the maximum position to which the spring extends x_m. Record this position.

$x_m =$ _____ cm

Call the point halfway between x_m and x_0, $x_{1/2m}$. Release the 0.5 kg mass from the x_0 position. Watch it as it passes through the midpoint in the extension $(x_{1/2m})$. Is the loss in gravitational potential energy equal to the gain in elastic potential energy at an extension of $x_{1/2m}$? Discuss.

(b) Calculate the loss in gravitational potential energy of the 0.5 kg mass as it falls from x_0 to $x_{1/2m}$ in joules.

(c) Calculate the gain in elastic potential energy of the spring as it extends from x_0 to $x_{1/2m}$ in joules.

(d) Compare the loss in gravitational potential energy with the gain in elastic potential energy at the half extension point. Predict where the difference is. Briefly outline an experimental procedure you could follow to verify your prediction.

6. Assume $g = 10$ N/kg in the following problem.

A mass of 1.0 kg is attached to the free end of a spring having a force constant $K = 10$ N/m. When the 1.0 kg mass is released from the zero extension point (x_0) the spring elongates to a maximum extension of 2.0 m.

(a) Assume the spring is elongated to an extension of 2.0 m and released. Complete the following table to determine the elastic and gravitational potential energy of the system at 0.25 m extension intervals. Continue the analysis until the spring returns to zero extension.

(b) Calculate the sum of the elastic and gravitational potential energies at the different heights of the mass above the maximum stretch position. Enter these in the table.

Gravitational potl.energy		Elastic potential energy			
Height above maximum stretch point h (m)	$Ug = mgh$ (joules)	Extension x (m)	Extension^2 x^2 (m)^2	$Ue = \frac{1}{2}kx^2$ (joules)	Total energy $Ug + Ue$ (joules)
0	0	2.0			
.25		1.75			
.50		1.50			
.75		1.25			
1.00		1.00			
1.25		.75			
1.50		.50			
1.75		.25			
2.00		0			

(c) Plot on the same axis a graph of:

    (i) gravitational potential energy of mass versus extension of spring

    (ii) elastic potential energy of spring versus extension of spring

    (iii) total potential energy of system versus extension of spring

(d) At what extension of the spring is the potential energy of the system at its minimum? How many joules of potential energy have disappeared? Neglecting the mass of the spring, determine the speed of the 1 kg mass at a spring extension of 1.0 m. Show the calculations.

CONVERSIONS OF MECHANICAL ENERGY   **Expt. #52**

When an object is dropped through a vertical distance Δh near the earth's surface, it loses gravitational potential energy. Some of this energy is converted to kinetic energy as evidenced by an increase in the velocity of the falling object. This experiment is a study of the transfer between the potential energy and the kinetic energy in a system where some parts move in a different direction to others.   **Introduction**

To study the mechanical energy present in a closed system.   **Purpose**

Apparatus

175

Method

1. Fasten a timer at one end of a level lab table. Place a cart loaded with 2 bricks next to it. Attach a pulley to the opposite end of the bench at the same height as the cart. Fasten a second pulley about 1 m directly above the first. Tie a light cord to the cart, passing it along the table and through the 2 pulleys.

2. Add masses to the free end of the cord next to the upper pulley tapping the cart with each addition until the cart and its load move across the table with a uniform speed. Record the mass required to overcome friction.

3. Attach an additional mass of about 1 kg to the free end of the cord. Attach a paper tape to the cart and through the timer. Pull the cart back to the timer, activate the timer and release the system.

4. Determine the mass of the cart and 2 bricks in kg by using a suitable balance. The simple meter stick balance and a standard kg mass studied in Experiment 6 can be used. Record the mass added to cause the acceleration in kg.

5. Choose 2 ticks on the paper tape separated by a distance interval of about 1 m. Measure the distance travelled by the cart in a time of 1 tick at the beginning and end of this interval. Determine the time in seconds equivalent to 1 tick and, using this and the distance travelled in 1 tick, calculate the speed of the cart in m/sec at the beginning and end of this distance.

6. Calculate the kinetic energy of the total system of cart, bricks and falling masses at the beginning and end of the 1 m interval. From this determine the change in kinetic energy of the system in joules.

7. Carefully measure the distance (in m) between the 2 ticks chosen in Part 5. This represents the distance fallen by the mass added in Part 3 to cause the acceleration of the system. Calculate the potential energy change of this mass in falling through this distance. Use the value of $g = 9.8$ N/kg.

8. Compare the loss in potential energy of the mass with the gain in kinetic energy of the system. Calculate the per cent difference between the lost potential energy and the gained kinetic energy. Is there a significant difference? Account for any difference.

   Why did we not include the lost potential energy of the mass that produced the constant velocity, in our comparison with the gained kinetic energy? Where did the lost potential energy of this mass go?

9. Write a word equation for this experiment to illustrate the conservation of mechanical energy. State the Law of Conservation of Energy. Suggest ways of improving the accuracy of this experiment.

10. A 1.3 kg cart rests on a smooth table. A light cord attached to the cart hangs over a frictionless pulley at the edge of the table and has a 0.4 kg mass attached to the free end. Determine the velocity of the cart after it has travelled 1.0 m from the release point by applying the Law of Conservation of Energy.

Unit IV

ELECTRICITY
AND
ATOMIC STRUCTURE

Expt. #53   THE MILLIKAN EXPERIMENT

Apparatus

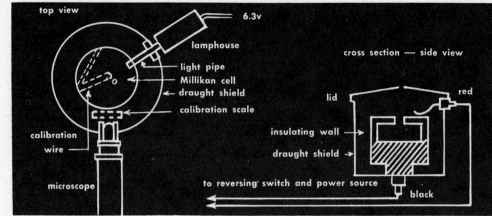

Introduction   A sphere falling through a medium experiences a viscous drag in dynes $\left(\dfrac{\text{g-cm}}{\text{sec}^2}\right)$ equal to $6\,\pi\,rnv$ (Stoke's Law) where r is the sphere radius in cm, n is the viscosity of the medium in poises, and v is the velocity of the sphere relative to the medium in cm/sec. A terminal velocity U is reached when this force is equal to the apparent weight of the sphere (i.e., its true weight less the buoyant force).

Since *mass = volume × density*,

and *weight or force of gravity = mass × acceleration due to gravity*,

therefore, *apparent weight = volume × apparent density × acceleration due to gravity*.

The volume of a sphere is $\frac{4}{3}\pi r^3$,

therefore, apparent weight $= \frac{4}{3}\pi r^3\,(p - \delta)\,g$

Hence $\frac{4}{3}\pi r^3\,(p - \delta)\,g = 6\,\pi r\,n\,U$

or, rearranging and solving for r^2,

$$r^2 = \frac{9\,n\,U}{2\,(p - \delta)\,g} \qquad (1)$$

where p = density of the sphere material,

δ = density of the medium, in this case air, and

g = acceleration due to gravity in cm/sec².

This equation will permit us to determine the radius of the sphere used in this experiment by measuring the sphere's terminal velocity.

If the sphere carries a charge q and is between parallel metal plates a distance d apart to which a potential difference of V is applied, it experiences an electrical force equal to $\dfrac{qV}{d}$. It is therefore possible to hold the sphere stationary (i.e., balanced) when the electrical force on the sphere is equal in magnitude, but opposite in direction to its apparent weight.

Therefore $\dfrac{qV}{d} = \frac{1}{3}\,\pi r^3\,(p - \delta)\,g$

or, on substituting $6\,\pi r\,n\,U$ for $\frac{1}{3}\,\pi r^3\,(p - \delta)\,g$

we obtain $\dfrac{qV}{d} = 6\,\pi r\,n\,U$

and arranging, $$\boxed{q = \dfrac{6\,\pi r\,n\,U\,d}{V}} \qquad (2)$$

Since r, n, U and d are constants for a given drop, the quantity of charge on the drop is inversely proportional to the potential difference V, which produces a balanced condition $q \propto \dfrac{1}{V}$.

In order to show that the charges on a small sphere bear a small whole number ratio to one another, it is necessary, therefore, to show that the balancing voltages bear a small whole number ratio to one another. The largest balancing voltage must be balancing the sphere in its condition of least charge.

Furthermore, by applying equation (2) and knowing the radius of the sphere from equation (1) it is possible to determine the quantity of charge on the sphere for different balancing voltages. A number of measurements can be made on one drop under different conditions of charge, or, alternatively, measurements on a series of different drops can be made, but the radius of each drop would have to be determined each time.

The sphere in this experiment may be either a very small oil drop produced by an atomising spray, or a plastic sphere of known radius. The sphere enters the space between the parallel plates by means of a tiny hole in the upper plate and its position is observed with a microscope by the light it scatters. It appears as a bright spot of light which rises in the field of view as the sphere falls. The sphere radius may be determined from (1) by measuring the time the spot of light takes to move between two rulings on the microscope scale and hence calculating the terminal velocity U. If the air through which the sphere falls is ionised, the sphere may collect one or more ions of either sign and so become charged. It can then be caused to rise between the plates (i.e., move downwards in the field of view) by applying to the plates a large enough potential difference of the right kind (either positive or negative). To enable this to be done, a variable supply of direct current (d.c.) is supplied together with a special reversing switch having a central position N at which the plates are connected together.

1. Set up the Millikan cell on a stand in a level position.

2. Connect the light source and adjust it to focus at the center of the plates of the Millikan cell. Place a fine wire probe vertically at the midpoint in the cell and adjust the eye piece of the microscope to bring the scale and the wire in sharp focus. Remove the wire.

3. Connect the circuit as suggested by the manufacturer, *but be careful*. The voltage used should be 300-500 volts d.c. Adjust the potential difference to within this voltage range and set the reversing switch in the neutral position (N).

4. Position the nozzle of the bulb of the atomizer so that, on squeezing, it causes some of the spheres to enter the Millikan cell through the hole at the top. Spots of light scattered by these spheres should be seen rising in the field of view as they fall. Operate the reversing switch in each direction to find out if any of the spheres are charged sufficiently for their direction of motion to be reversed. If none are, return the switch to its neutral position and hold a radioactive source for a moment or two (*using a source handling tool*) over the hole where the spheres were inserted. Test again for the presence of charged spheres. Repeat until charged spheres are obtained.

5. Select one sphere and, by using the reversing switch in the appropriate direction, quickly adjust the potential difference applied until the sphere comes to rest in the lower half of the field of view. Make any necessary adjustment to the microscope position to focus the drop. Observe carefully for a minute and make any necessary adjustments to the potential difference so that the spot of light does not show any regular drift up or down. Record this balancing potential difference.

6. Allow the sphere to fall freely by switching to the neutral position and time the light spot as it crosses a known number of scale spaces. As soon as timing is complete, restore the balancing potential difference and record the time taken.

7. Repeat Parts 5 and 6 if time allows.

8. Now attempt to change the charge on the sphere. With the sphere balanced, hold the radioactive source (*using a source handling tool*) over the hole and switch to neutral position. After a moment or two, restore the balancing potential difference and observe whether the sphere is still balanced. If it is, then no charge change has occurred and the process should be repeated. When a change has taken place, rebalance the sphere and remove the source.

9. Repeat Parts 5, 6 and 8

10. Continue this process until measurements of 5 different charges have been made. Alternatively, or if the sphere is lost, measurements on a series of different drops can be made. In this case, repeat Parts 3, 4, 5 and 6 for each drop.

11. Set the reversing switch to its neutral position. Place a thermometer with its bulb in contact with the Millikan cell and record the temperature of the apparatus. This will enable you to determine the density of air at this temperature by referring to tables.

12. To calibrate the scale, focus the microscope on a mm ruler and determine the number of scale spaces corresponding to a known number of divisions. Calculate the drop radius, (if this is unknown) and hence the quantity of charge q on the drop. From this obtain a value for the elementary electrical charge e.

13. Write up your results in the form of a formal laboratory report as indicated by your instructor. Do not be discouraged if you find difficulty in taking readings and analyzing the results.

CHARGE TRAVEL IN IONIC SOLUTIONS   Expt. #54

Introduction

The transfer of charge in a metal conductor is due to the movement of negative elementary charge. But current can also be transferred through a solution containing charged atoms called ions.

The quantity of charge transferred in a conductor is directly proportional to both the current flowing and the time of flow, or $Q = I\,t$, where

Q = number of elementary charges transferred in coulombs

I = rate of flow of charge in coulombs/sec (amperes)

t = time of flow in seconds

In this experiment we will use two electrolytic cells, one containing copper sulphate solution and the other a silver thiosulphate solution in order to study how charge is transferred in solutions. To ensure that the same current passes through both solutions for the same length of time, thereby transferring the same amount of charge, we will connect both cells in series to the same source of electrical power.

Purpose

To determine how charge is transferred in ionic solutions.

Apparatus

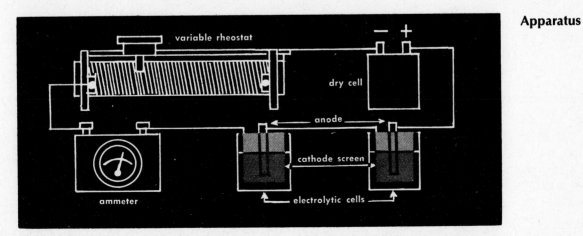

Special Materials

Copper electrolyte solution—prepared by dissolving 50 g of bluestone and 12 milliliters (ml) of concentrated sulphuric acid in 240 ml of water.

Silver electrolyte solution—prepared by dissolving 42.5 g of sodium thiosulphate, 5.5 g of sodium metabisulphite, 5.5 g of anhydrous sodium sulphate, 6.5 g of anhydrous sodium acetate, and 10 g of pulverized silver chloride in 250 ml of water. Warm the solution to a temperature no greater than 35°C to aid in dissolving. The silver may be replenished for no more than 4 consecutive runs by adding 4 g of silver chloride per 250 ml of solution after each 30-minute run.

Cathodes—made from 6 × 16 cm of 20 mesh copper wire gauze rolled into a cylinder with about 1 cm of overlap. Clean the surface of the copper by dipping into a solution placed beneath a hood consisting of 1 part concentrated hydrochloric acid, 25 parts concentrated nitric acid, 145 parts concentrated sulphuric acid, and 165 parts water for about 5 seconds. Rinse with water immediately. The screen to be used as the cathode for silver plating must be submerged in the silver electrolyte for about 10 minutes, then washed in water, dipped in alcohol and allowed to dry.

Method

1. Remove any grease from the surfaces of the copper screen cylinder and the silver-coated copper screen cylinder by first rinsing them in water and then in alcohol. Let them dry.

   Determine the mass of each of these clean dry screen cylinders to the nearest 0.01 g by using a suitable balance and record in the table provided.

2. (a) Place about 200 ml of the copper sulphate solution in a 250 ml beaker and suspend the copper screen cylinder in this solution to serve as the cathode.

   Suspend a sheet of copper wound in a spiral, or a copper wire wound into a tight coil, in the solution in the center of the beaker but not touching the cylinder to serve as the anode.

   (b) Place about 200 ml of silver thiosulphate solution in another 250 ml beaker and suspend the silver-coated copper screen cylinder in this solution to serve as the cathode. A strip of lead suspended in the center of the solution will serve as the anode. *Rinse your hands immediately to remove any silver electrolyte which causes stains to hands and clothing.*

3. Connect the electrolytic cells in series with each other and with a 6-volt power supply, a rheostat, an ammeter and an open switch. The wire screens must be acting as the cathodes in each cell. Adjust the rheostat to give maximum resistance. Have your instructor check your setup before proceeding any further.

4. Close the switch and record the time to the nearest second. Quickly adjust the current to 1 ampere by adjusting the rheostat. Let the current flow for 30 minutes. Watch the ammeter and maintain the current as close to 1 ampere as possible by adjusting the rheostat.

5. Record the time to the nearest second as you open the switch. Remove the wire screen cathodes and rinse each gently by dipping in a beaker of cold water. Rinse the cathodes in alcohol to remove the water droplets. Allow them to dry for about 3 minutes. Find the mass of each cathode to the nearest 0.01 g using the same balance as used in Part 1.

Mass (g)	Cathode from copper sulphate solution	Cathode from silver thiosulphate solution
Final		
Initial		
Change		

Current (amperes)	Time (sec)	Charge transferred (coulombs)

6. (a) Describe the deposit on the cathode removed from the copper sulphate solution. What is this deposit? Calculate the mass of the deposited material.

Assuming the material deposited is copper, use the atomic mass of copper (63.5) and Avogadro's Number (6.023×10^{23}) to determine the number of copper atoms deposited. Show your calculations below.

(b) Describe the deposit that has formed on the cathode from the silver thiosulphate solution. What is this deposit? Calculate the mass of the deposited material.

Assuming the material deposited is silver, use the atomic mass of silver (108) and Avogadro's Number to determine the number of silver atoms deposited. Show your calculations below.

(c) How many atoms of silver were deposited for every atom of copper deposited? If each silver ion in solution carries 1 elementary charge, how many elementary charges does each copper ion carry?

7. To cross-check the number of elementary charges carried by the silver and copper ions, respectively:

(a) Calculate the number of elementary charges transferred during the experiment (1 coulomb of charge = 6.25×10^{18} elementary electrical charges).

(b) Calculate the number of elementary charges carried by each copper ion. What assumption was necessary to enable you to determine this?

(c) Calculate the number of elementary charges carried by each silver ion.

(d) Compare the number of elementary charges carried by the silver and copper ions. How does this compare with the result from Part 6 (c)?

(e) What was the sign of the charge transferred by the copper and silver ions? Why?

8. Briefly describe how this apparatus could be used to determine the relation-

ship between mass (m) of material deposited and quantity (Q) of charge transferred. What kind of relationship do you think this would be?

9. Briefly describe how this apparatus could be used to measure the current flow in a series circuit. Include any precautions that should be followed for accurate results.

10. A spoon is silver-plated by electrolytic methods, using a current of 0.10 ampere. It has a surface area of 20 cm² on which a coating of silver 0.0010 cm thick is plated. The density of the silver is 10.5 gm/cubic centimeter (cc).

(a) How many g of silver are deposited?

(b) How many coulombs of electricity pass through the solution?

(c) How long did it take to electroplate the spoon?

Expt. #55   EMISSION SPECTRA

Introduction   When a solid or liquid is heated to incandescence, it emits a continuous spectrum. For example, the heated tungsten filament in a showcase bulb produces this type of spectrum. When monatomic molecules of a gas or vapor are excited by heating or by an electrical discharge, they do not emit a continuous spectrum but rather a line (incomplete) spectrum having the colors of the continuous spectrum where the lines are visible and with dark gaps of missing colors in between.

When molecules of gas made up of more than one atom are excited without separating into atoms, a band spectrum is produced made up of many separate lines, so numerous and so close together that they appear as bands.

You have probably seen the dazzling white light emitted by burning magnesium or the blue color of burning sulphur. Does every different heated element emit its own particular spectrum? To determine this we will excite compounds containing the elements to be studied by heating them in the flame of a Bunsen burner.

Purpose   To study the emission spectra of different elements using first the naked eye, and then a hand spectroscope.

Apparatus

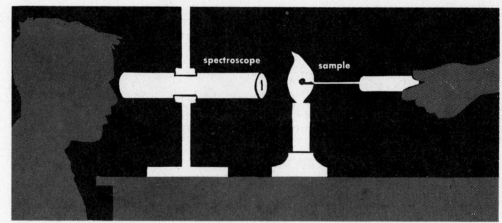

Method   1. (a) View the light from a showcase bulb with the unaided eye from a distance of about 1 m. Enter the color seen in the table provided.

(b) The unaided eye cannot distinguish the component colors contributing to the predominant color observed. The spectroscope, containing a diffraction grating which splits light into its component colors, will enable us to do this. Clamp the spectroscope horizontally to a retort stand. Look at the showcase bulb through the spectroscope. What do you see directly in the center of the field of view? This is the image of the slit of the spectroscope.

List the colors you see on each side of this central band in the order in which they appear. To spread the spectrum out as much as possible, be sure the slit is parallel to the lines on the grating.

2. (a) We will excite the materials to be tested using the hot flame of a Bunsen burner. Light the burner and adjust it to produce a hot, almost colorless, flame. Heat the tip of a clean nichrome wire in the flame, and then dip it quickly into the material to be tested. Begin with sodium chloride. Insert the tip containing the material into the flame and note the predominant color(s) imparted to the flame as seen with the unaided eye. Enter the color(s) in the table.

   (b) View the flame of the Bunsen burner through the spectroscope from a distance of about 0.5 m with the slit parallel to the flame. Place the wire containing the sample of sodium chloride into the flame. List the color(s) seen in the table provided.

   (c) Repeat procedures (a) and (b) for the other compounds listed under Part 2 in the table. Use a different clean nichrome wire for each compound, marking the compound name on the handle of the rod.

   How do the colors imparted to the flame by the chlorides of sodium, potassium and copper compare with the nitrates of these elements?

   Are the colors characteristic of sodium, potassium and copper or of the chlorides and nitrates?

3. Mix a small amount of sodium chloride in a large amount of lithium chloride. Look at the color imparted to the flame with the unaided eye and then with the spectroscope. List the observed color(s) in the table. How does this spectrum compare with the individual spectra of sodium chloride and lithium chloride? What use could be made of a flame test?

4. Perform flame tests on baking soda and chalk dust, listing the observed colors. What element does baking soda contain? Why?

What element does chalk dust contain?

| Part | Material viewed | Color observed | | Type of emission spectra |
		Unaided eye	Spectroscope	
1	Showcase bulb			
2	Sodium chloride			
	nitrate			
	Potassium chloride			
	nitrate			
	Cupric chloride			
	nitrate			
	Calcium chloride			
	Strontium chloride			
	Lithium chloride			
3	Mixture of sodium chloride and lithium chloride			
4	Baking soda			
	Chalk dust			

5. Discharge tubes containing the following gases or vapors will be set up at the front of the room by your instructor. As you view them, list the colors observed with the unaided eye and with the spectroscope. Name the category of emission spectra each falls into.

| Gas or vapour | Colors observed | | Type of spectra |
	Unaided eye	Spectroscope	
Neon			
Argon			
Helium			
Mercury			
Nitrogen			
Hydrogen			
Water vapour			
Chlorine			
Carbon dioxide			

6. Distinguish clearly between the different kinds of emission spectra using an example for each.

~~~~~~ ●

ABSORPTION SPECTRA   Expt. #56

The emission spectra observed in the previous experiment were produced when light from incandescent sources travelled directly to the spectroscope. The colors in these spectra were determined by the source emitting the light. When light from an incandescent solid or liquid source passes through a colored vapor, gas, solution or solid before reaching the spectroscope, certain colors are absorbed from the continuous spectrum. The resulting spectrum is called the absorption spectrum of the material through which the light passes. The three types of absorption spectra are (a) continuous, (b) band and (c) line.

Introduction

To study the nature of absorption spectra.

Purpose

Apparatus

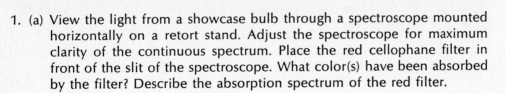

1. (a) View the light from a showcase bulb through a spectroscope mounted horizontally on a retort stand. Adjust the spectroscope for maximum clarity of the continuous spectrum. Place the red cellophane filter in front of the slit of the spectroscope. What color(s) have been absorbed by the filter? Describe the absorption spectrum of the red filter.

Method

(b) Place the blue filter in front of the slit. Compare the absorption spectrum of the blue filter with that of the red filter. These are both examples of continuous absorption spectra.

2. Make a dilute solution of potassium permanganate and water. What color does it appear to the unaided eye?

   Place the solution between the spectroscope and the showcase bulb with the slit of the spectroscope close to the solution. View the filament of the light bulb. What color(s) have been absorbed from the continuous spectrum? Describe the absorption spectrum of potassium permanganate solution. This is an example of an absorption band spectrum.

3. Clamp the spectroscope horizontally to a retort stand. Place the flame of the Bunsen burner about 10 cm from and directly in line with the slit of the spectroscope. Cover a showcase bulb with a cylinder of cardboard containing a slit about 3 cm long and 0.5 cm wide. Adjust the position of the showcase bulb until all the white light from the slit of the showcase bulb passes through the Bunsen burner flame before entering the spectroscope. (A lens will permit you to do this.) Clamp it in this position. Turn the showcase bulb off. Using a nichrome wire, heat some sodium chloride in the flame. Observe the line spectrum of sodium. Turn on the white light source. Do you see any break in the yellow region of the continuous spectrum at the location of the line spectrum of sodium? Look carefully. This is the line absorption spectrum of sodium.

   Turn off the showcase bulb suddenly, but leave the sodium in the flame. What takes the place of the dark line in the previous spectrum? Why should a dark line be present with white light incident on the slit?

4. Decrease the width of the slit in the spectroscope with black masking tape until it is about 0.5 mm in width. Look at a white cloud in bright sunlight through the spectroscope. The spectrum may at first appear continuous. Study the various regions. Can you see any breaks in the continuous spectrum? These will appear as dark lines called Fraunhofer lines. In what regions of the spectrum can you see these lines? This is another example of a line absorption spectrum.

5. Describe a method employing absorption spectra that scientists use to determine the elements present in the outer cool layers around the sun. Use the library to obtain the information.

6. Describe an experiment you could perform (including the apparatus you would need) to determine the nature of the absorption spectrum of chlorophyl.

A DIMENSION OF A MOLECULE   **Expt. #57**

Because of their microscopic size, it is difficult to measure atoms or molecules with the naked eye using a direct method such as a micrometer screw gauge. The indirect method outlined below using metal shot or glass beads will permit us to obtain results to an order of magnitude.

Introduction

Let us consider an individual metal shot as representing one molecule. We will then pour enough metal shot into a flat dish until we have a layer one shot thick. By transferring this metal shot to a graduated cylinder, we can read the volume. By using a ruler we can measure the cross-sectional diameter of the inner surface of the dish and calculate its area.

Volume of shot = _____

Inside diameter of dish = _____

Area of plate (πr^2) = _____

How can we use these measurements to calculate the diameter (or thickness) of one piece of shot?

In former experiments we have stressed the need for cross-checking. With metal shot this is a simple matter. Use a micrometer screw gauge and measure the diameter of a number of shots. Record these values and calculate the average diameter. This is a *direct* method.

Shot number	Diameter	Average diameter
1		
2		
3		
4		
5		

How does this value compare with the value obtained by the *indirect* method using the dish?

In the indirect method just outlined a single layer of closely packed particles was necessary. A single layer of molecules can be obtained by placing a drop of oleic acid on the surface of water using an eye dropper. Since the oleic acid is less dense than water and insoluble, it floats, spreading out until it reaches the edges of the container or until it becomes one molecule thick.

Since the size of the water surface is limited in this experiment, the amount of oleic acid present in one drop must be decreased. The oleic acid is therefore dissolved in a solvent such as alcohol. When a drop of the oleic acid–alcohol solution hits the water, the alcohol dissolves in the water, or evaporates, leaving behind the smaller volume of oleic acid to spread out, forming a film that we will assume to be one molecule thick.

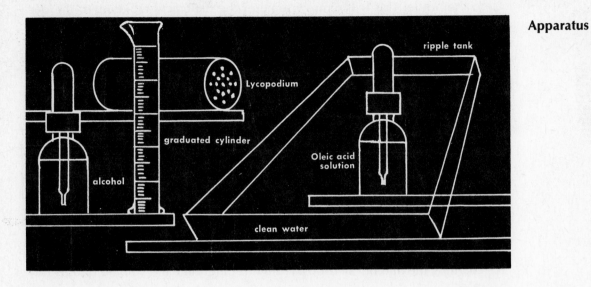

1. Thoroughly clean the ripple tank as follows: One student holds the tank at **Method**
   an angle over the sink while a second student slowly pours a stream of
   water over it using a beaker. A third student cleans the bottom and sides
   using a clean paper towel.

2. Fill the tank to a depth of 1 cm with clean water.

3. The instructor will dust a thin film of lycopodium powder on the surface of
   the water.

4. Carefully add a drop or two of alcohol to the center of the tank using the
   eyedropper. (*Do not place the eyedropper for the alcohol in the oleic acid
   bottle.*) What do you observe immediately the alcohol hits the water?

   What happens a short time after this?

   What happens to the alcohol that was added?

   Explain both observations.

5. When using the oleic acid eyedropper and bottle use the following procedure. Return the first couple of drops of oleic acid from the eyedropper
to the bottle. This will remove some of the oleic acid adhering to the outside of the dropper and thus minimize any variation in the size of the later
drops. With the eyedropper of oleic acid close to, but not touching, the
surface of the water, add 1 drop of oleic acid solution. Measure the average
diameter of the film produced. Add another drop, measure the new
diameter and repeat this with 3 drops. Using these values, calculate the
area of the film.

Number of drops	Average diameter	Area of film
1		
2		
3		

6. Add drops of oleic acid solution to a graduated cylinder until 1 cc is present,
counting the number of drops. From this determine the volume of one drop
in cc.

Calculations 1. Concentration of oleic acid solution

Solution #1
Add 5 cc of pure oleic acid to 95 cc of alcohol. What fraction of solution
#1 is pure oleic acid?

Solution #2
Add 5 cc of solution #1 to 45 cc of alcohol. What fraction of solution #2
is solution #1?

By referring back to the fractional concentration of oleic acid in solution
#1, determine the fractional concentration of oleic acid in alcohol of solu-
tion #2.

2. *Volume of pure oleic acid in 1 drop of solution*
   Using the volume of 1 drop of oleic acid solution #2 and the fractional concentration of oleic acid in alcohol of this solution, determine the volume of pure oleic acid in 1 drop (in cc).

3. *Thickness of oleic acid film*
   Assuming the oleic acid film is in the shape of a cylinder and using the same technique as was used to determine the diameter of the metal shot, determine the thickness of the oleic acid film.

4. Compare the average wavelength of white light to the thickness of the oleic acid molecule to an order of magnitude. Will white light diffract appreciably around the edges of an oleic acid molecule?

5. Indicate the approximate accuracy achieved in the various measurements in this experiment.

6. Suggest ways of minimizing the errors encountered in this experiment.

~~~~~~ ●

THE PHOTOELECTRIC EFFECT   **Expt. #58**

A great similarity exists between the properties of light and water waves. For example, both light and water waves reflect, refract, diffract and interfere. Can all the properties of light be accounted for by assuming that it travels as a wave?   **Introduction**

Taylor's experiment on the graininess of light complicates this theory. In this experiment we will study another property of light which cannot be satisfactorily explained using the wave model.

Purpose To study the emission of elementary charges from metallic surfaces using electromagnetic radiation.

Apparatus

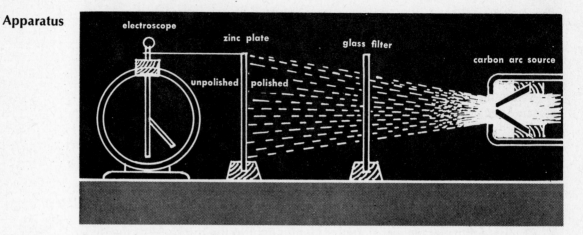

Method

1. Clean and polish a sheet of zinc with sandpaper or emery cloth. Place it on an insulated stand and attach it to the knob of a metal leaf electroscope. Charge the system positive and then negative. Observe the rate of convergence of the leaves. If the leaves do converge, record the time to converge completely from a given divergence.

2. Recharge the zinc plate and electroscope system, if necessary, with a positive charge. Shine the light from a covered carbon arc source on the shiny zinc surface. Do you notice any significant change in the electroscope leaves?

   Remove the glass filter from in front of the carbon arc source. Do not look directly at it with the naked eye. Do you notice any significant change in the leaves?

3. Recharge the zinc plate and electroscope system negatively. Shine the light from the covered carbon arc source on the shiny zinc surface. Do you notice any significant change?

Remove the glass from in front of the light source. What do you observe happening? What kind of charged particles must be leaving the zinc surface? How do you know that ions are not coming to the zinc plate from the air? What kind of light does not pass through glass but causes the emission? Will light in the visible region of the electromagnetic spectrum cause emission with zinc? Discuss.

PLANCK'S CONSTANT   Expt. #59

Introduction

The photoelectric effect in metals, as indicated in the last experiment, is the emission of electrons from a surface using light energy. The wavelength of the incident light must be less than a certain limit for each particular material, or the frequency must be greater than a certain threshold value. This is called the threshold frequency.

Since no significant predictable delay is observed, even when very feeble light of the required frequency is used, we must assume that light energy travels in the form of bundles or quanta having both wave and particle properties. A bundle or quanta of a certain minimum energy will cause the emission of electrons from a given substance. The energy of a quanta of light must be related in some manner to its frequency or wavelength.

The following data was obtained using equipment too costly for the ordinary high school laboratory. By analyzing the data, you should be able to arrive at the expression relating the energy of an incident photon and its frequency. We will make the assumption that the kinetic energy of the highest energy photoelectrons emitted is directly proportional to the energy of the incident photons. Are we justified in making this assumption? Discuss.

The apparatus consists of a phototube containing a cathode made of barium, which has a low work function energy making it sensitive to light, even in the visible part of the spectrum. The collector for the emitted electrons, the anode, and the cathode are located within a well-evacuated glass container, but connected to the outside by conducting terminals. These terminals are connected in parallel to a variable voltage source permitting variations in the voltage between the anode and the cathode from +0.5 volts to −2.0 volts in small steps. A sensitive microammeter is connected in series and enables us to measure the current flow in the circuit and, therefore, the number of electrons reaching the anode.

By decreasing the plate voltage until no more current flows in the circuit, we reach a point where the electrical energy in electron volts supplied by the source is equal to the kinetic energy of the highest energy emitted electrons, forcing them back into the cathode. We can convert energy in electron-volts to joules by using the conversion factor, 1 electron-volt = 1.6×10^{-19} joules.

Purpose To determine the relationship between the energy of the incident photons (or highest energy photoelectrons) and the frequency of the incident light.

Apparatus

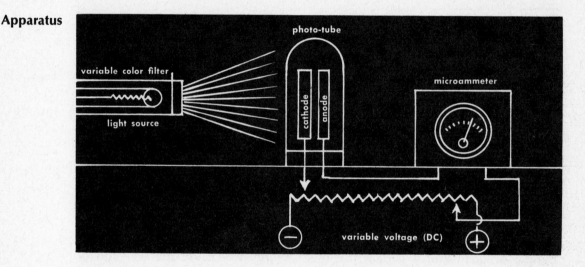

Information A monochromatic light source of constant intensity was focused on the cathode of the phototube described above. As the voltage was decreased in small steps from an initial value of +0.5 volts, voltage and the corresponding current readings were taken until a zero current was recorded on the microammeter. The voltage at which this occurs is called the cutoff voltage and corresponds to the energy of the highest kinetic energy photoelectrons in electron volts.

This procedure was repeated with the initial monochromatic source but using a lower intensity of light. The procedure was then repeated using other monochromatic light sources, one violet, one green and one yellow.

The data collected are shown in Table I.

Analysis 1. Plot a graph of current on the y axis versus voltage on the x axis, including all the above data on one graph.

What feature of the graph gives an indication of the intensity of the incident light or the number of incident photons/unit time/unit area?

Wavelength	Violet 4060 Å		Violet 4360 Å	Green 5460 Å	Yellow 5780 Å	**Table I**
Voltage V (volts)	High intensity Current I (amperes) × 10⁻⁹	Low intensity Current I (amperes) × 10⁻⁹	Current I (amperes) × 10⁻⁹	Current I (amperes) × 10⁻⁹	Current I (amperes) × 10⁻⁹	

Voltage V (volts)	High intensity $I \times 10^{-9}$	Low intensity $I \times 10^{-9}$	$I \times 10^{-9}$	$I \times 10^{-9}$	$I \times 10^{-9}$
.50	55.0	26.7	51.0	59.0	15.0
.30	54.0	26.6	50.0	58.0	14.8
.10	50.0	25.6	48.0	56.0	14.2
.00	45.0	24.0	43.0	52.0	12.3
−.05				46.0	9.7
−.10				33.2	7.4
−.15				27.8	5.2
−.20	38.0	19.0	34.0	22.0	3.4
−.25				16.0	2.0
−.30				12.0	0.6
−.35				7.6	0.0
−.40	28.0	13.5	21.0	4.0	0.0
−.45				0.0	0.0
−.60	19.8	7.8	10.8		
−.80	10.2	3.7	3.3		
−.90	6.0	2.6	1.4		
−1.00	3.6	1.6	0.3		
−1.05	2.6	1.2	0.0		
−1.10	2.0	1.0	0.0		
−1.20	0.6	0.3			
−1.25	0.0	0.0			
−1.30	0.0	0.0			

Which color of light used had the highest intensity? Which color had the lowest intensity?

Does the intensity of the light used change the cutoff voltage? What does this suggest?

Explain why the current for each color of light used levelled off as the voltage was made positive. How could the current flowing at a given voltage be increased?

2. (a) Tabulate the cutoff voltage for each wavelength of light used in Table II. Calculate the frequency and include this in the table.

Table II

Light color	Wavelength λ (Å)	Frequency v (vps)	Cutoff voltage	Maximum kinetic energy of photoelectrons in	
				E_k (electron -volts)	E_k (joules)
Violet	4060				
Violet	4360				
Green	5460				
Yellow	5780				

(b) Which wavelength photons have the highest energy per particle? How do you know?

(c) Plot a graph of cutoff voltage against wavelength (λ). Describe the graph.

Plot a graph of cutoff voltage against frequency (v). Describe the graph. What relationship seems to exist between these two variables?

3. (a) Calculate the maximum kinetic energy of the photoelectrons in units of electron-volts and joules and enter in Table II.

(b) Plot a graph of the maximum kinetic energy of the ejected photoelectrons in joules versus frequency. To simplify the graph, use standard form for the numbers on the axes. For example, the kinetic energy could be expressed as a number $x\ 10^{-19}$ joules and the frequency as a number $x\ 10^{14}$ vib/sec. Number the axes so that you can determine the x and y intercepts.

Describe the graph. What relationship exists between maximum kinetic energy of the photoelectrons and frequency? What relationship exists between the energy of the bombarding photons and their frequency? Why?

(c) The general equation for a straight line is $y = mx + b$ where:

y = ordinate value
x = abscissa value
m = slope
b = y intercept

(i) Determine the value of the slope of this graph. Show the calculations including units. This slope is called "Planck's Constant" (h). The accepted value is 6.62×10^{-34} joule-sec.

(ii) Pick corresponding values for x and y from the graph. Substitute these and the value you calculated for Planck's Constant into the equation to determine the y intercept (b). The intercept measures the work function energy of the metal used in the cathode and is independent of the type of light used. How many joules of energy must an incident photon have before it can cause photoelectric emission with barium? To what is this equivalent in electron-volts?

(iii) What is the lowest frequency of light that will cause photoelectric emission? This is indicated by the x intercept on the graph and is called the threshold frequency of the metal. To what wavelength of light does this correspond?

(iv) Write the general equation describing the graph using the symbols established for the variables. Define the meaning of each symbol.

4. The data in Table III was obtained using a phototube with a cesium-coated cathode and the same monochromatic light sources.

Table III

Wavelength λ (Å)	Frequency ν (vps)	Maximum kinetic energy of photoelectrons (joules)
4060	7.4×10^{14}	2.6×10^{-19}
4360	6.89×10^{14}	2.2×10^{-19}
5460	5.5×10^{14}	1.3×10^{-19}
5780	5.2×10^{14}	1.1×10^{-19}

(a) Plot this data on the graph used in Part 3. How do the slopes of the two lines compare? What does this indicate about Planck's Constant?

Use this graph to determine:

(i) the threshold frequency for cesium

(ii) the work function energy or B value for cesium.

(b) Which material, barium or cesium, should be used for maximum emission of electrons in the visible range of the spectrum? Why?

~~~~~~ ●

THE ENERGY LEVELS OF STANDING WAVES   Expt. #60

Introduction

Both the Franck-Hertz experiment and the definite line spectra given off by excited elements indicate the existence of a characteristic set of energy levels for each different atom. In order to explain this using the wave-particle duality of matter and radiation, we must make use of the matter waves associated with particles. What type of waves do not radiate energy away but hold a fixed energy shape relationship for a period of time?

In Experiment 27, we created standing waves in a linear medium by sending two identical wave trains in the opposite direction through the same place. Can this type of wave serve as a model to help us visualize a mechanism to explain the stable energy levels of an atom such as hydrogen?

Purpose

To study standing waves in various media as a satisfactory model for the stable atomic energy levels in the hydrogen atom.

Apparatus

circle of rubber tubing   point source

PART A
Method

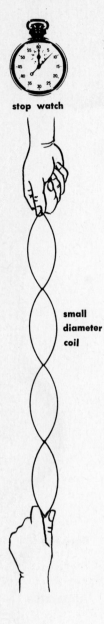

stop watch

small diameter coil

1. While your partner holds one end of the small diameter coil rigid, give it some tension. Record the stretched length (*d*) in the table below. Produce periodic travelling waves of low frequency by vibrating your hand very slowly back and forth at right angles to the axis of the coil and rolling your hand in the direction of the coil's motion. How many wave trains are travelling along the coil's length at any instant?

Vary the frequency of the coil until it vibrates in 1 loop and continues this motion with little addition of energy on your part. Stop vibrating your hand. Describe the resulting motion of the coil. Does it hold the energy for long? If friction was absent, describe the motion you would expect. Is energy escaping from the coil, neglecting frictional effects?

Again vibrate the coil to produce a standing wave with 1 loop of length (*d*). Determine the time for a number of vibrations and from this calculate the frequency. Determine the wavelength of the travelling waves producing the standing wave and record.

2. Increase the frequency from that used in Part 1 until the coil vibrates first in 2 loops and then in 3 loops. Determine the frequency and wavelength of the travelling waves producing the standing waves and enter the results in the table.

Length of coil = _____ m

Number of loops	Frequency of waves (*f*)	Wavelength of travelling waves (λ)	Velocity of travelling waves (*v*)
1			
2			
3			

Compare the speed of the travelling waves producing the 3-loop and 1-loop standing waves.

In order to produce the 3-loop standing wave pattern, by what factor must the frequency used to produce 1-loop standing waves be changed? What change has occurred in the wavelength of the travelling waves with this change in frequency?

Recall that the energy carried by an electromagnetic wave of wavelength (λ) or frequency (v) is given by the expressions $E = \dfrac{h\,c}{\lambda} = h\,v$, where h and c are constants. Describe the standing wave pattern associated with the lowest possible stable energy level of the stretched coil of length (d). Does this coil have other definite, almost stable, energy levels? Discuss. Neglecting friction, can the coil hold these energies?

1. In order to study standing waves in a two-dimensional medium, place about 1 cm of water in a level ripple tank. Set up the wave generator with the single small point source touching the water in the center of a circular reflecting barrier of rubber tubing. Make sure the bulb is positioned so that it acts as a point source of light located directly above the vibrating point source.

   Adjust the wave generator to a low frequency. Watch the pattern on the screen inside the circular reflecting barrier. Increase the frequency gradually. Can you obtain a pulsating stationary pattern? Have you produced standing waves? If so describe them. About how many wavelengths are present across the radius of the reflecting barrier?

2. Double the frequency of the generator. What happens to the wavelength? Is a standing wave pattern now present in the ripple tank? If so, how does it differ from the former pattern?

Describe the pattern you would expect within the circular reflecting barrier at half the initial frequency used.

Are there definite energy levels associated with standing water waves? If so, is there a lowest stable energy level? Discuss.

3. Do standing waves provide a satisfactory model for the stable energy levels and the lowest energy level in the hydrogen atom? Discuss. (Refer to your textbook before answering.) If so, do the standing waves studied in this experiment provide a satisfactory model? Discuss.